SHARKS

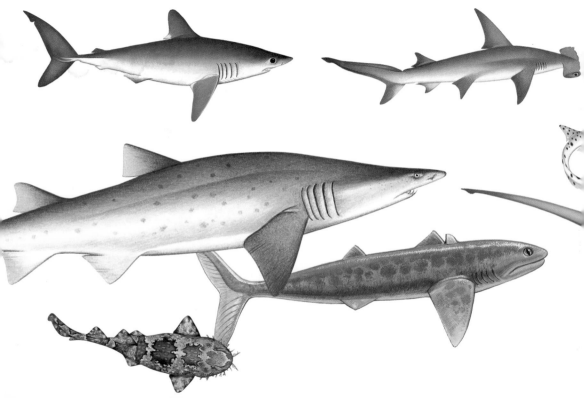

SHARKS

Consultant Editor
Leighton Taylor

FOG CITY PRESS

Published by Fog City Press
415 Jackson Street
San Francisco, CA 94111 USA

Copyright © 2008 Weldon Owen
This edition printed 2008

Chief Executive Officer, Weldon Owen Group: John Owen
President, Chief Executive Officer, Weldon Owen Inc.: Terry Newell
Vice President, International Sales: Stuart Laurence
Vice President, Publisher: Roger Shaw
Vice President, Creative Director: Gaye Allen
Vice President, Sales and Business Development: Amy Kaneko
Executive Editor: Mariah Bear
Managing Editor: Karen Perez
Project Editor: Lucie Parker
Contributing Editors: Frances Reade, Rachel Sarah
Art Director: William Mack
Series Designer: Nika Markovtzev
Project Designer: Andreas Schueller
Production Director: Chris Hemesath
Production Manager: Michelle Duggan
Cover Design: Bret Hansen

Library of Congress Control Number: 2008934950

ISBN-13: 978-1-74089-849-2

Color reproduction by SC (Sang Choy) International Pte. Ltd.
Printed by SNP Leefung Printers Ltd.
Printed in China

A Weldon Owen Production

Contents

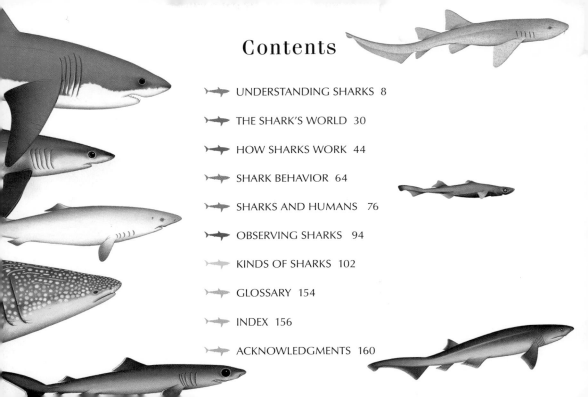

UNDERSTANDING
SHARKS

Toothed Torpedo

When most people think of sharks, they imagine huge, aggressive great whites, with fearsome teeth and gaping jaws, tearing through the water after helpless prey. Not all sharks are scary beasts, though—in fact, sharks are really just fishes! Like all fishes, they use slits in their sides, called gills, to breathe oxygen underwater, and they swim along by swinging their bodies and tails from side to side.

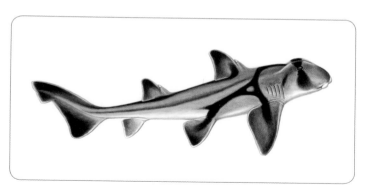

FRIEND OR FOE
Despite their bad reputations, not all sharks are dangerous to people. For example, this Port Jackson shark spends most of its time hanging out on the ocean floor, and won't hurt anyone—unless someone bothers it first.

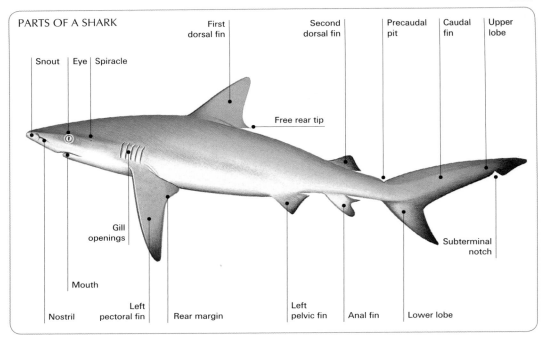

PARTS OF A SHARK

First dorsal fin

Second dorsal fin

Precaudal pit

Caudal fin

Upper lobe

Snout

Eye

Spiracle

Free rear tip

Gill openings

Subterminal notch

Mouth

Nostril

Left pectoral fin

Rear margin

Left pelvic fin

Anal fin

Lower lobe

A Fish Apart

While sharks have a lot in common with other fishes, they do have some special traits. First, most fishes have skeletons of dense, heavy bone, but sharks' skeletons are made of a softer, more flexible tissue called cartilage that helps them stay afloat. Also, sharks' gills appear on the outside of their bodies, while most other fishes' gills are hidden, protected by plates of thick bone. As for skin, fishes usually gleam with an armor of scales, but sharkskin is rough, like sandpaper.

FINNED RELATIVES
The fish family is a big one, with 30,000 different species living in every kind of watery habitat, from the ocean depths to wetlands. Fishes vary in size from tiny gobies less than half an inch (1 cm) in length to the whale shark, which can grow to 46 feet (14 m).

HEFTY SWIMMER

An air pouch called a swim bladder keeps this heavy, bony fish from sinking in the water.

LIGHTWEIGHT CRUISER

The shark's skeleton of elastic-like cartilage makes it light and buoyant, keeping it afloat.

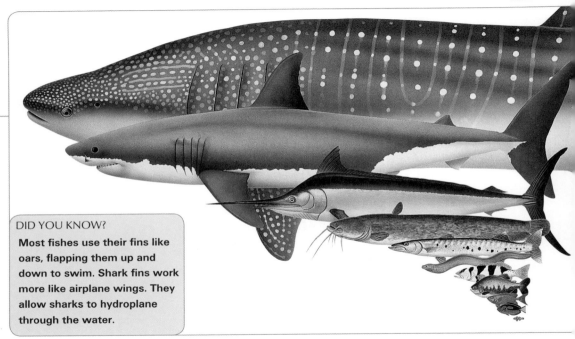

DID YOU KNOW?

Most fishes use their fins like oars, flapping them up and down to swim. Shark fins work more like airplane wings. They allow sharks to hydroplane through the water.

All Shapes and Sizes

Slender and sleek, stout and bulky, or flattened like pancakes—sharks come in many shapes, and in many sizes. The average shark only grows to be about 30 inches (75 cm) in length; in fact, more than 80 percent of sharks are smaller than adult human beings. Only about 4 percent of sharks ever reach gigantic proportions, growing from 13 to more than 39 feet (4–12 m) long. This variety in shape and size helps different species survive in different ocean habitats—from deep waters to shallow lagoons.

FROM MINIATURE TO MIGHTY
This small selection of shark species, drawn to scale and compared with the size of a human diver, provides a glimpse of sharks' diversity.

REEF HUNTER
The gray reef shark has a stocky body, growing up to 6 feet (1.8 m) long. It stalks prey along reefs in the Pacific and Indian Oceans.

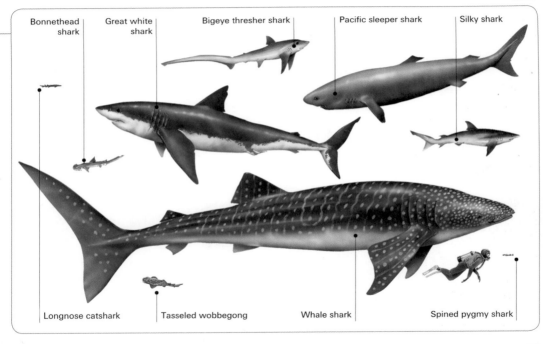

Bonnethead shark

Great white shark

Bigeye thresher shark

Pacific sleeper shark

Silky shark

Longnose catshark

Tasseled wobbegong

Whale shark

Spined pygmy shark

The First Sharks

Sharks have inhabited the ocean for more than 400 million years, yet the sharks of today still look much like their ancient ancestors. Their origins, however, are shrouded in mystery. Because most of a shark's skeleton is too soft to fossilize, full shark fossils are rare, making it difficult for scientists to learn much about the earliest sharks. But the hard parts, like teeth and fin spines, fossilize easily. Scientists have found many teeth fossils, partly because sharks lose and replace their teeth throughout their lives.

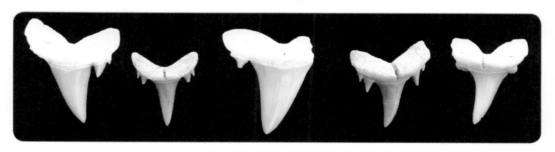

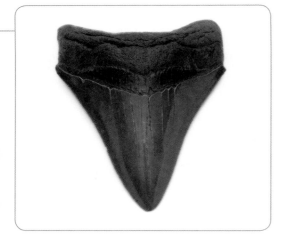

The long-extinct *Cladoselache* was probably a powerful predator, well adapted for feeding on fast fishes.

One of the smallest shark species, the tiny spined pygmy shark shares many features with ancestral sharks.

The whale shark, the largest living shark species, exhibits the tried-and-true body shape of many modern sharks.

THE SHAPE OF SUCCESS

Long before dinosaurs ruled the world, sharks had evolved their basic streamlined shape. Because it works well for them, this shape has hardly changed since the Devonian Period, about 400 million years ago. Different species, however, have specialized shapes for their environments.

The Typical Shark

Although sharks come in many shapes and sizes, most people consider requiem sharks to be the most typical, like the blue shark on the opposite page. It has a lean body, a long snout and pectoral fins, and a tail fin with an upper lobe that's longer on top than bottom. The narrow head and wide body make it easy for the shark to turn quickly.

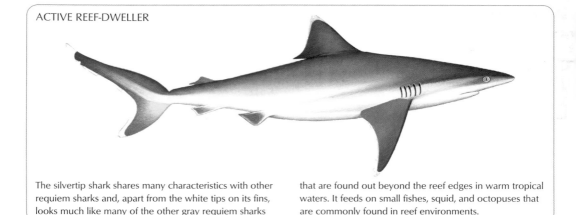

ACTIVE REEF-DWELLER

The silvertip shark shares many characteristics with other requiem sharks and, apart from the white tips on its fins, looks much like many of the other gray requiem sharks that are found out beyond the reef edges in warm tropical waters. It feeds on small fishes, squid, and octopuses that are commonly found in reef environments.

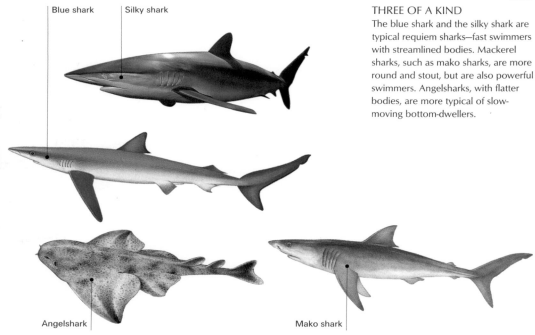

Blue shark | Silky shark

Angelshark

Mako shark

THREE OF A KIND
The blue shark and the silky shark are typical requiem sharks—fast swimmers with streamlined bodies. Mackerel sharks, such as mako sharks, are more round and stout, but are also powerful swimmers. Angelsharks, with flatter bodies, are more typical of slow-moving bottom-dwellers.

How Sharks Adapt

You can tell a lot about a shark's way of life by looking at how it's shaped and the way it swims and moves.

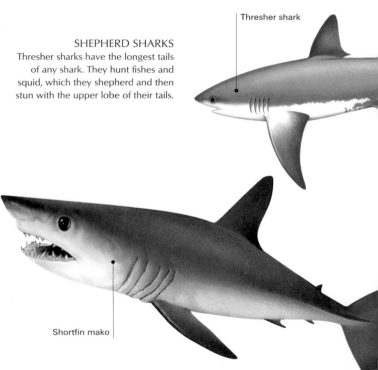

Thresher shark

SHEPHERD SHARKS
Thresher sharks have the longest tails of any shark. They hunt fishes and squid, which they shepherd and then stun with the upper lobe of their tails.

SPEEDY MAKO
The mako is probably the fastest and most active of all sharks. It is more stout than the typical shark and has evolved a shape that's perfect for fast swimming.

Shortfin mako

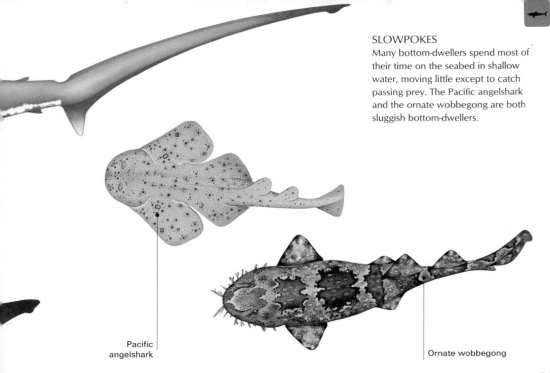

SLOWPOKES

Many bottom-dwellers spend most of their time on the seabed in shallow water, moving little except to catch passing prey. The Pacific angelshark and the ornate wobbegong are both sluggish bottom-dwellers.

Pacific angelshark

Ornate wobbegong

Oddities of the Ocean

Evolution has given some sharks extreme, and even bizarre, body shapes. They developed these fascinating features as adaptations to their environments and their needs.

FUNNY FACES

Great hammerhead shark

Goblin shark

The hammerhead shark uses the strange, wing-like growths on its face to perform fast hairpin turns, while the goblin shark's unique snout helps it detect prey in deep, dark waters, where prey is hard to see.

UNUSUAL FEEDING BEHAVIOR

Also known as the cigar shark, the cookiecutter shark has jaws and lips that form a suction cup on the skin of its prey. It bites and swivels, using its teeth to gouge out chunks of flesh, just like the pastry tool! Their scars have been seen on large fishes, marine mammals, and even submarines.

Cookiecutter shark

Sawshark

SPIKY SNOUT

The sawshark can be quickly identified by its sawlike snout and distinctive pair of barbels. These sharks probably use their snouts to disable their victims.

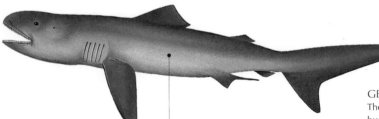

Megamouth shark

GENTLE GIANT

The rare megamouth shark has huge jaws, which it uses to scoop up plankton and very small fishes.

23

Close Cousins

Similar to sharks are rays and chimeras, two fish groups that also have cartilaginous skeletons. Rays are essentially "flat" or "winged" sharks that use their disc-like bodies to glide through water and hide in sand. Bottom-dwelling chimeras, however, do not look very sharklike: they evolved into a distinct family about 340 million years ago.

SHARK RELATIVES
Rays are the sharks' closest relatives. They are mainly classified by their snouts (which are either sawlike or rounded), the number and location of their dorsal fins, and whether or not they have electric organs, or stingers.

SEA RODENT

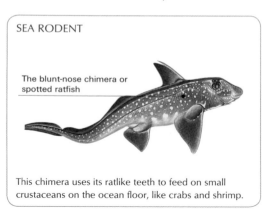

The blunt-nose chimera or spotted ratfish

This chimera uses its ratlike teeth to feed on small crustaceans on the ocean floor, like crabs and shrimp.

CLEVER CAMOUFLAGE

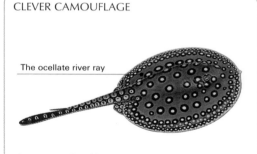

The ocellate river ray

The pattern of eyelike spots on this ray helps it hide in pebbles and mud on the river bottom.

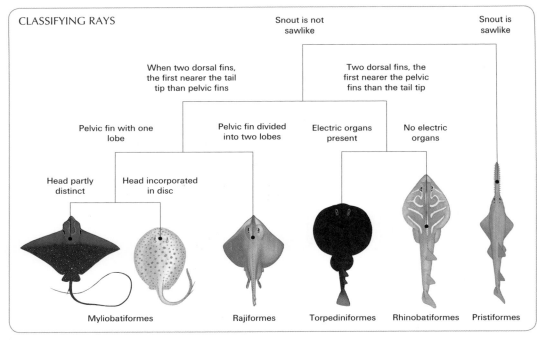

CLASSIFYING RAYS

Snout is not sawlike

Snout is sawlike

When two dorsal fins, the first nearer the tail tip than pelvic fins

Two dorsal fins, the first nearer the pelvic fins than the tail tip

Pelvic fin with one lobe

Pelvic fin divided into two lobes

Electric organs present

No electric organs

Head partly distinct

Head incorporated in disc

Myliobatiformes

Rajiformes

Torpediniformes

Rhinobatiformes

Pristiformes

What Is a Ray?

Long ago, rays looked like sharks, but their pectoral fins
eventually grew into wing-like shapes that enable their
underwater "flight" and help them hunt prey on the sea
bottom. Like sharks, the 600 ray species are very diverse.
They grow from 4 inches (10 cm) to more than 18 feet (6 m)
long, and their shapes vary according to their lifestyles.

THE PARTS OF A RAY
The ray's eyes are on top of its flat
body, while its mouth and nostrils
are found on the bottom. Some
rays have stinging spines that they
use to stun unsuspecting fishes.

POLKA DOTS
Some rays, such as this bluespotted
ribbontail ray, have striking looks.
While pretty, this ray is armed and
dangerous—it has two venomous
spikes on its tail.

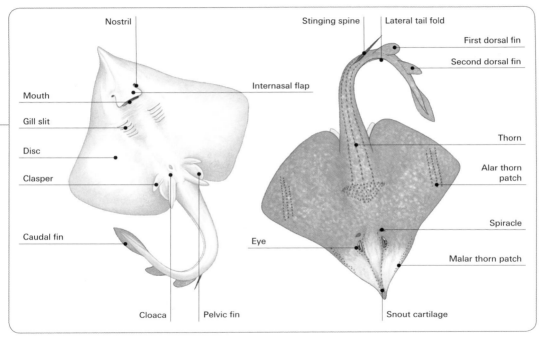

Nostril

Mouth

Gill slit

Disc

Clasper

Caudal fin

Internasal flap

Stinging spine

Lateral tail fold

First dorsal fin

Second dorsal fin

Thorn

Alar thorn patch

Spiracle

Eye

Malar thorn patch

Cloaca

Pelvic fin

Snout cartilage

How Rays Move

The body shapes of rays have become highly modified and specialized over the years. They are flattened, and the pectoral fins and body are joined to form a distinctive structure known as the "disc."

DID YOU KNOW?

Some rays can skip along the ocean's surface, and others can even leap clear out of the water.

FLYING FISHES
Rays flap their large pectoral fins up and down to glide through the water. This motion looks similar to a bird in flight.

THE SHARK'S WORLD

Where Sharks Live

Sharks inhabit almost every marine ecosystem on Earth and are distributed throughout all the world's oceans. Many live in temperate and tropical seas, and near the coasts of islands and continents. There are few species in the upper reaches of the open ocean and even fewer in very deep water.

LIFE ON THE REEF
The reefs along island and continental coastlines are teeming with small fishes, crustaceans, and squids that sharks—such as this gray reef shark—enjoy snacking on.

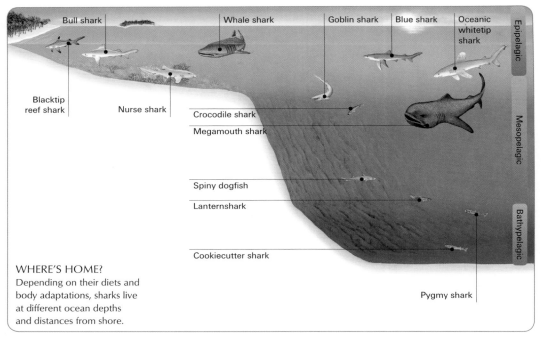

Bull shark

Whale shark

Goblin shark

Blue shark

Oceanic whitetip shark

Blacktip reef shark

Nurse shark

Crocodile shark

Megamouth shark

Spiny dogfish

Lanternshark

Cookiecutter shark

Pygmy shark

Epipelagic

Mesopelagic

Bathypelagic

WHERE'S HOME?
Depending on their diets and body adaptations, sharks live at different ocean depths and distances from shore.

Active Tropical Sharks

Sharks can be grouped by the temperature of water that they prefer: tropical, temperate, or cold. Sharks abound in the marine waters of the coastal tropics, where the temperature is 70°F (21°C). Active tropical sharks include the requiem sharks, the hammerhead sharks, the wobbegongs, and the nurse and whale sharks. They swim constantly, traveling long distances to find food and migrating to bask in warm waters.

PLANKTON FEEDER
The whale shark is often found near the surface in tropical waters, where it filter feeds on plankton.

Bottom-Dwelling Tropical Sharks

Unlike active tropical sharks, bottom-dwelling tropical species spend their time on the ocean floor, moving only to hunt. Many do not hunt at all—they just sit, camouflaged, on the seafloor, waiting for a meal to come to them. When it does, they dart out, grab it, eat it, and then continue to wait. Many bottom-dwellers never travel more than a few miles from where they were born. Most tropical bottom-dwellers are small, rarely growing more than 6 feet (2 m) long.

LONGTAILED CARPETSHARKS
The epaulette shark is a type of longtailed carpetshark, which is a bottom-dwelling shark known for "walking" on the ocean floor. These spotty sharks are common on coral and rocky reefs and in tide pools.

EPAULETTE SHARK

LIVING LARGE

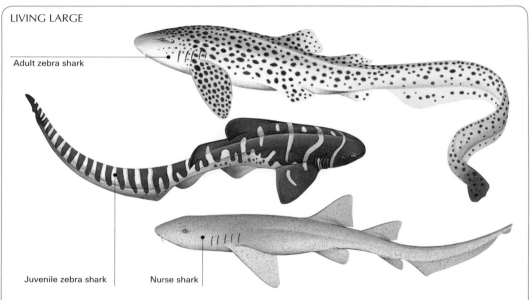

Adult zebra shark

Juvenile zebra shark

Nurse shark

These bottom-dwelling tropical sharks grow much larger, and travel much farther, than most of their relatives. They can grow to 15 feet (5 m) long. The zebra shark is named for the black stripes it has when young; as it ages, it grows spots.

Sharks of the Pacific Reefs

Pacific reef ecosystems provide a home for several species of shark. These reefs support many tasty creatures for sharks to feed on, including fishes, crustaceans, squid, and octopuses. Different sharks live and hunt in different parts of the reef.

PACIFIC COMMUNITY

While many shark species frequent the tropical Pacific reefs, the most common visitor is the blacktip reef shark, which sometimes swims in water so shallow that its dorsal fin is exposed above the surface. The largest shark on most Pacific reefs is the tiger shark. It can grow to be more than 16 feet (5 m) long.

REEF DWELLER

Whitetip reef sharks live almost exclusively on coral reefs in the Indian and Pacific oceans. They use their pointed, cusped teeth to pull fishes out of hiding places in reef crevices.

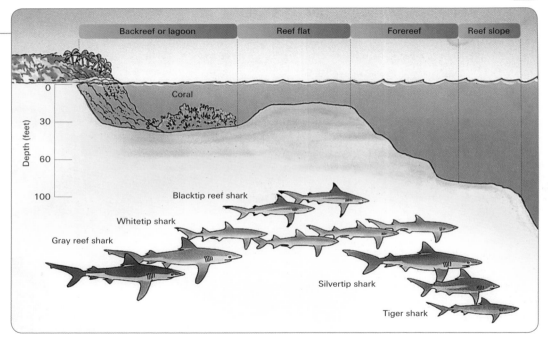

Backreef or lagoon   Reef flat   Forereef   Reef slope

Depth (feet)

0

30

60

100

Coral

Blacktip reef shark

Whitetip shark

Gray reef shark

Silvertip shark

Tiger shark

Temperate-Water Sharks

Temperate-water sharks live mostly at water temperatures between 50 and 70°F (10–21°C). Like tropical sharks, some are active swimmers and some are bottom-dwellers. Many active species are large sharks that are widely distributed, like the sand tiger shark. Bottom-dwellers, such as the longnose sawshark, are small and stay close to their birthplaces.

DIFFERENT STROKES
The great white shark is a large shark that roams widely throughout regions of temperate, tropical, and cold water. By contrast, the bottom-dwelling Port Jackson shark's travels are much more restricted, due to its limited diet.

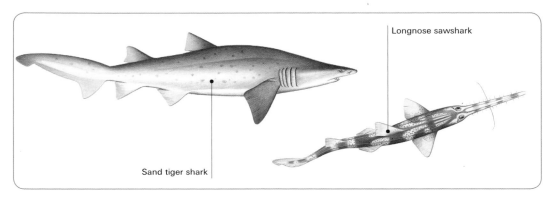

Longnose sawshark

Sand tiger shark

Great white shark

Port Jackson shark

Cold-Water Sharks

Cold-water sharks inhabit waters colder than 50°F (10°C). Many of them live very far north or south, in or close to Arctic or Antarctic waters. Others live in the deep, cold waters of temperate, and even tropical, regions. Just like tropical-water and temperate-water sharks, these sharks can be divided into active swimmers and bottom-dwellers.

LARGER ACTIVE SHARKS
Among the larger active cold-water sharks—those that grow to more than 6 feet (2 m) long—are the sixgill and sevengill sharks, the frilled shark, and the goblin shark. It is thought that many of these sharks travel great distances, because food is scarce in such cold waters.

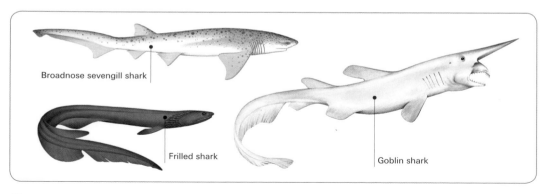

Broadnose sevengill shark

Frilled shark

Goblin shark

SLUGGISH GIANT

The Greenland sleeper shark grows to 23 feet (7 m) long. It is the only polar shark in the Atlantic and has even been found under ice floes! It is slow-moving and shows little resistance when captured. This shark prefers deep water, but when near freezing shores, it will swim in shallow waters.

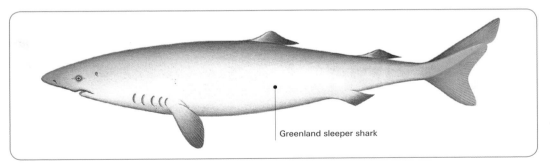

Greenland sleeper shark

HOW SHARKS WORK

Built for Speed

A shark's skeleton is made of cartilage, which weighs less and is more flexible than bone. These lightweight frames help sharks swim quickly and stay buoyant in the ocean. Some people think shark cartilage has medicinal benefits; this belief contributes to the overfishing of sharks in some areas.

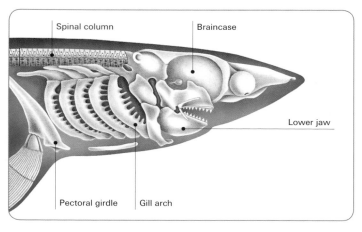

Spinal column

Braincase

Lower jaw

Pectoral girdle

Gill arch

A SHARK'S HEAD
This diagram shows the main features of a shark's head. The spinal column runs the length of the body, connecting to the top of the caudal fin (also called the tail).

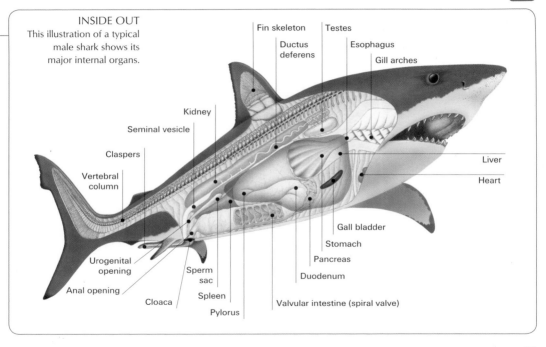

INSIDE OUT
This illustration of a typical male shark shows its major internal organs.

Fin skeleton
Ductus deferens
Testes
Esophagus
Gill arches
Kidney
Seminal vesicle
Claspers
Vertebral column
Liver
Heart
Urogenital opening
Sperm sac
Anal opening
Spleen
Cloaca
Pylorus
Gall bladder
Stomach
Pancreas
Duodenum
Valvular intestine (spiral valve)

Breathing Underwater

Like humans, sharks need oxygen to survive. Instead of lungs, they use gills to pull oxygen from water and to breathe out carbon dioxide. Active sharks (such as requiem sharks) swim constantly, which keeps oxygen-rich water flowing into their mouths and over their gills. Less active sharks (like bottom-dwellers) have a pump that pulls water through their gills.

HOW A SHARK BREATHES
Oxygen-rich water enters the mouth and passes over the gills, which pull oxygen from the water. The oxygen-depleted water then passes out through the gill slits. Meanwhile, the shark's heart pumps blood into the gill arches, where it absorbs the crucial oxygen.

RESPIRATION HELPERS
When this whale shark breathes out carbon dioxide, its open gills reveal the thin, plate-like gill filaments just inside. These filaments absorb oxygen and supply it to the shark's body.

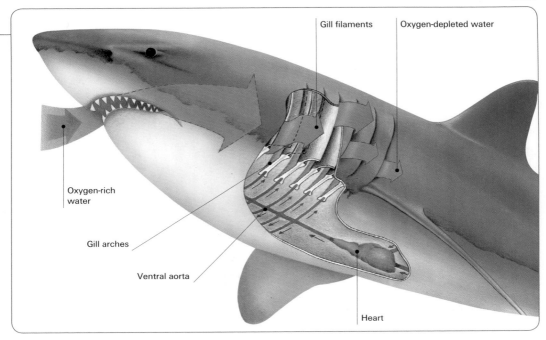

Gill filaments

Oxygen-depleted water

Oxygen-rich water

Gill arches

Ventral aorta

Heart

49

Deep-Sea Senses

Sharks have all the traditional senses that humans do: touch, taste, smell, sight, and hearing. In particular, sharks are well known for their acute sense of smell, which allows them to sniff down prey from many miles away. Good hearing also helps sharks on the hunt: if another animal is injured, a shark will follow its sounds of struggle and pick up an easy meal.

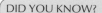

SPECIAL SNIFFER
The Port Jackson shark has an unusual piglike snout. The extra folds in its skin help it find food on the sandy seafloor.

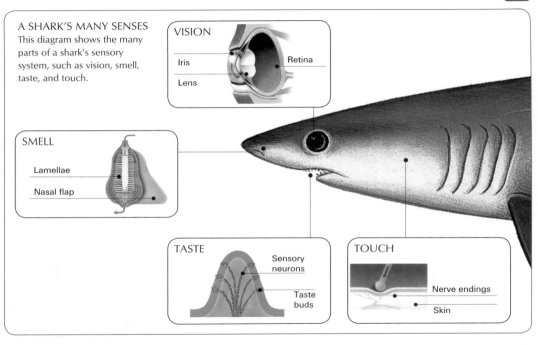

A SHARK'S MANY SENSES
This diagram shows the many parts of a shark's sensory system, such as vision, smell, taste, and touch.

VISION
Iris
Lens
Retina

SMELL
Lamellae
Nasal flap

TASTE
Sensory neurons
Taste buds

TOUCH
Nerve endings
Skin

Special Senses

In addition to the five traditional senses, sharks have unique and mysterious ways of observing and responding to their worlds. For example, sharks have a pair of sensitive tubes, called a lateral line, that run along their sides under their skin. Pores in their skin connect to the lateral line, sending important messages and allowing sharks to feel faint vibrations in the water made by prey or potential predators. Sharks also have special organs called ampullae of Lorenzini in their snouts. These organs look like little pores, and are sensitive to weak electric signals put out by other creatures. They help sharks detect and find prey over small distances. This important tool is called electrosense, and it works even when prey is buried in sand!

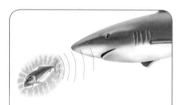

IN SEARCH OF PREY
Electrosense is one of sharks most powerful tools. The small pores on their snouts (called ampullae of Lorenzini) help them seek out food.

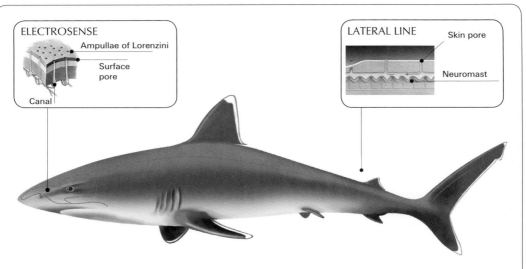

ELECTROSENSE

Ampullae of Lorenzini

Surface pore

Canal

LATERAL LINE

Skin pore

Neuromast

The red line on this shark's body shows its lateral line, an important part of the nervous system that collects information from the shark's surroundings. When the skin is stimulated, a hair cell called a neuromast passes a message onto the lateral line, which then communicates with the shark's brain. The ampullae of Lorenzini found in sharks' snouts also transmit outside information to nerves beneath the skin.

Tail Power

The tail, or caudal fin, is what moves most sharks through the water, propelling them forward by swinging from side to side. Tail sizes and shapes vary depending on the species, but most shark tails have two lobes, and the upper lobe is usually much bigger than the lower one. The size and shape of a shark's caudal fin is often a key to whether or not a shark has a busy, active lifestyle, or a sluggish, inactive one.

VARIATIONS ON A THEME
The tails of tiger and nurse sharks look most like the tails of ancient sharks. The thresher shark uses its long tail to strike prey. The porbeagle's short tail helps it cruise slowly, then suddenly speed up. The dangerous oceanic whitetip is identified by its white tail markings, while the cookiecutter's tail is typical of an active deepwater shark.

MAJOR MOTION
A whale shark has an enormous, powerful caudal fin. It needs this giant tail to thrust its huge body forward.

TIGER SHARK

NURSE SHARK
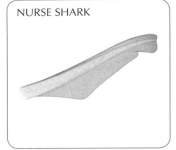

THRESHER SHARK
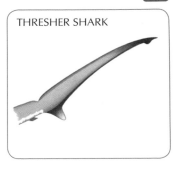

PORBEAGLE SHARK

OCEANIC WHITETIP SHARK

COOKIECUTTER SHARK

Fancy Fins

Like their tails, the dorsal, pelvic, and pectoral fins of different sharks vary in size and shape, but they all do the same job—help sharks maintain balance and control the direction and speed of their movements as they swim.

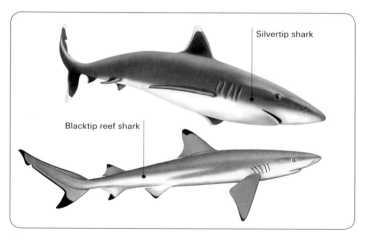

Silvertip shark

Blacktip reef shark

HORNED DORSALS
Some sharks have one dorsal fin, and some have two. The presence or absence of spines (or horns) on species that have two is an important feature. The whale shark and the Port Jackson shark both have two dorsal fins, but only the Port Jackson has distinct dorsal fin horns. Similarly, the horn shark has a horn on its fin.

BLACKTIPS AND SILVERTIPS
The blacktip reef shark is easily recognized by the black marks on its fins. The silvertip shark has distinctive white tips on all its fins.

WHALE SHARK

PORT JACKSON SHARK

HORN SHARK

CARPETSHARK

MEGAMOUTH SHARK

SILVERTIP SHARK

Snapping Jaws

The energy that sharks need for activities such as swimming must come from the food that they catch, so it is important that sharks are equipped with state-of-the-art hunting tools: jaws that can latch onto prey and teeth that can rip into meat. The modern shark has an upper jaw that can move away from the shark's skull when it bites, helping the shark get a grip on slippery prey that is trying to wiggle free.

The diagrams below show how a typical shark's jaw detaches from the skull as the shark attacks its prey. Right we see stages in the biting action of a great white shark: in stage one, the mouth begins to open; in stage two, the snout lifts as the upper jaw sticks out; in stage three, the lower jaw slips forward; and in stage four, it closes.

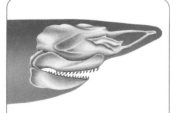

When at rest, the jaw is normally positioned below the skull.

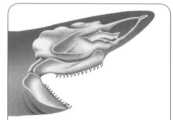

The jaw remains close to the skull as the mouth opens.

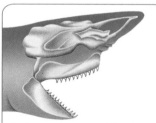

As the mouth opens wider, the upper jaw detaches from the skull.

STAGE ONE

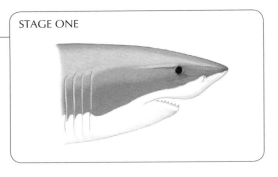

STAGE TWO

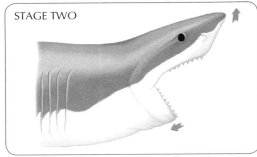

STAGE THREE

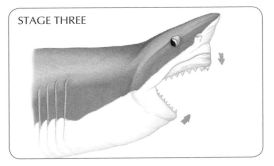

STAGE FOUR

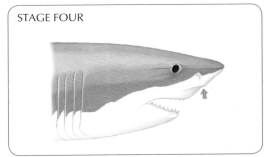

Terrifying Teeth

A shark's teeth are more than just weapons—without tentacles or fingers, teeth are sharks' main way of interacting with their environments. Shark teeth have a short life and are replaced as they break or wear down. Experiments with captive lemon sharks and horn sharks suggest that a tooth can last from under a month to a year before being replaced.

AN ARRAY OF SHAPES
These pictures give some idea of the variety of shark teeth shapes—from the long, sharp teeth of the goblin shark to the flat cobblestone-like patterns of the gummy shark's teeth, which are designed to crush rather than cut prey.

WHAT LARGE TEETH YOU HAVE
Great white sharks have up to 3,000 teeth at one time. They have five rows of teeth which rotate into place when needed. The front teeth are the largest; some grow as long as 3 inches (8 cm).

GOBLIN SHARK

GREAT WHITE SHARK

MILK SHARK

SALMON SHARK

TIGER SHARK

GUMMY SHARK

Skin-Deep Defense

A shark's skin protects from infection and damage, creates a streamlined texture that allows for speedy swimming, and outfits the shark with stealthy camouflage. Some sharks' skins even produce scales, teeth, spines, and horns! Sharks have different types of skin. For example, the skin of some deepwater gulper sharks and lanternsharks is thin and papery, while in the case of mature whale sharks the skin can be more than 1 inch (2.5 cm) thick and very tough.

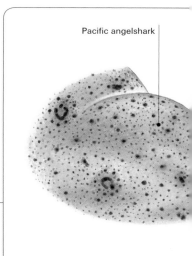

Pacific angelshark

SKIN PATTERNING
The speckled pattern on the Pacific angelshark's skin functions as camouflage, allowing the shark to hide on the seafloor. The spines on each of a horn shark's dorsal fins are formed by secretions from the inner and outer skin layers, and the bramble shark gets its name from its spiny growths.

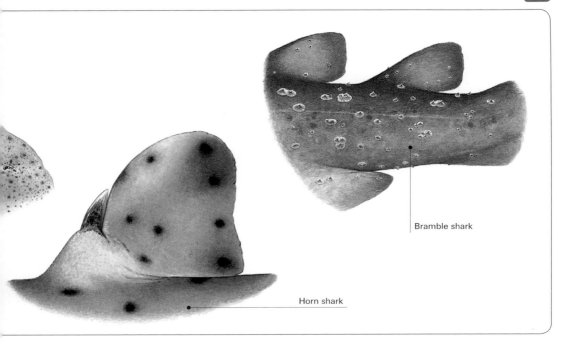

Bramble shark

Horn shark

SHARK BEHAVIOR

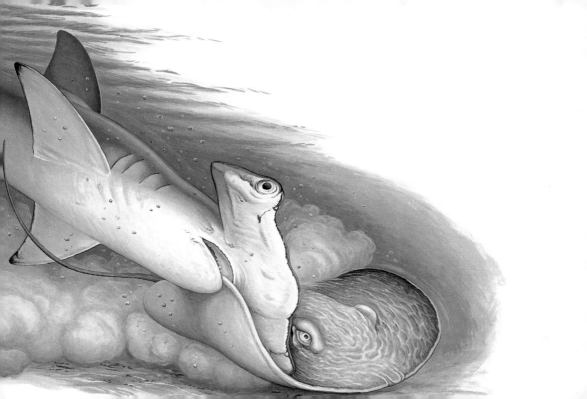

Feeding Frenzy, or Modest Meal?

Contrary to popular belief, sharks are not scavengers of the deep, feeding on everything that crosses their paths. Although few species have been studied in detail, it seems that sharks eat only what they need in order to survive, grow, and reproduce. Sharks are carnivores and consume a wide variety of food, ranging from tiny zooplankton to huge whales. Large active sharks may also eat rays, turtles, dolphins, seals, and even other sharks.

LUNCHTIME!
When hungry, the whale shark swims with its mouth wide open, gathering swells of small fishes in its mouth. This is called filter feeding.

SAVAGE SNACKING
The great white shark is famous for its hearty appetite! When it is young, it feeds on fishes, rays, and other sharks, but as it grows larger it moves onto seals, sea lions, and even small whales. If the meal is large enough, a great white shark may be satisfied for many months.

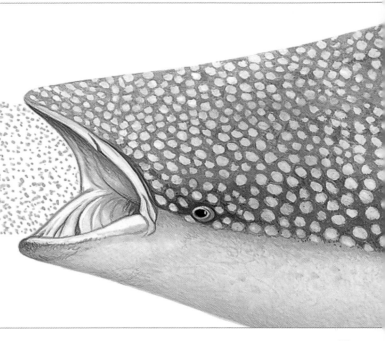

DID YOU KNOW?
Although cavernous and scary, the whale shark's huge mouth can be a safe place for fishes seeking shelter from more aggressive predators.

On Guard

Although sharks' main predators are other, larger sharks, smaller sharks face other dangers, and have strategies to protect them from attack or to scare off predators. Some have defenses on their bodies, like prickly spines. Others have more unique tactics, like the swellshark, which gulps water to puff up its body, making itself harder to swallow.

WARNING SIGNS
These illustrations compare the threatening displays of gray reef sharks with their normal behavior. This posturing has been observed in response to other sharks and humans.

CAVE HIDE OUTS
By day, whitetip reef sharks often rest in caves or under ledges, which provide them with maximum protection. At night, these sharks go out and become ferocious hunters.

THREATENING POSTURES

NONTHREATENING POSTURES

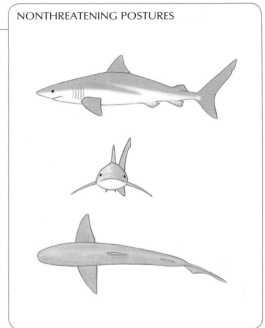

Solitary Creatures

It appears that sharks spend much of their lives on their own. For the most part, they hunt, feed, and live by themselves. We know that they do not form family groups or cooperate much with each other.

BUDDYING UP
While many sharks spend much of their time alone, some species, such as the scalloped hammerhead (right), are known to school, with the largest known school containing as many as 500 sharks. No one knows why they school, since they don't need to for safety or to hunt.

DANGEROUS LONER
The bull shark hunts alone and is extremely territorial, attacking humans, other sharks, and even horses and dogs. Many experts consider them to be the shark most dangerous to humans, and there is some speculation that attacks blamed on great white sharks were actually the work of bull sharks. These sharks have the unusual ability to swim in salt or fresh water, allowing them to travel thousands of miles up a river in search of prey.

From Egg to Shark Pup

Unlike most fishes, which give birth to hundreds of babies, sharks have a few babies at a time. Most sharks carry their eggs inside them, encased in membranes and nourished by yolks. Other sharks lay their eggs (wrapped in tough pouches) in protective areas, or anchor them to the seafloor. Some sharks carry their babies like mammals do, giving birth to them in safe "nursery" zones.

IN THE BEGINNING

Just after a shark egg is laid, the yolk is large and clearly visible. But you would need a magnifying glass to see the tiny shark embryo as it rests on top of the yolk.

NEARLY THERE

As the young shark absorbs the yolk and its nutrients, it gets larger and the yolk gets smaller. The growing baby shark breathes through well-developed gills.

HATCHING

When the young shark—called a pup—has developed enough, it hatches from its egg case. The shark is then on its own, and must be wary of becoming food.

CLEVER NESTING

Horn sharks lay oval-shaped, ridged egg cases. The mother wedges them into cracks and crevices, where the ridges hold them firmly and safely. Each species of horn shark lays a slightly different shape of egg case.

Riding the High Seas

Migration is an important part of life for many sharks. Most migrate annually to take advantage of ample food sources in different areas, and many migrate to mating zones where they meet with other sharks to reproduce. Others still journey to waters of preferred temperature when the seasons shift and the waters cool or warm. Some large species can make voyages of up to 1,000 miles (1,600 km). Scientists have learned about sharks' travels by tagging, which involves capturing a shark and attaching an electric device to it that, once it is released, will chronicle its journeys.

MARATHON SWIMMER
The record for the longest migration by a single shark is held by a blue shark that traveled 3,740 miles (6,000 km)! The shark was tagged off the coast of the United States, and was later recaptured 300 miles (500 km) south of the equator.

MAKO MOVEMENTS
The mako shark migrates individually each year from the northeast coast of the United States, where it passes the summer months, to wintering grounds in the warmer waters that stretch from the Gulf Stream to the Sargasso Sea.

BLUE SHARK AND MAKO SHARK MIGRATION PATTERNS

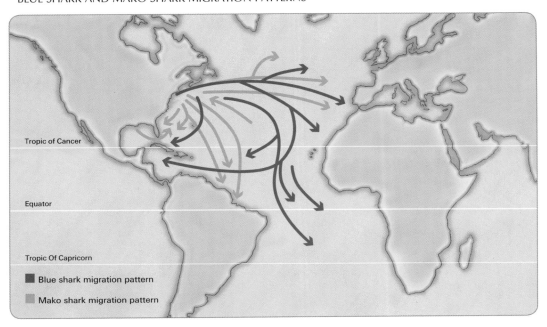

Tropic of Cancer

Equator

Tropic Of Capricorn

■ Blue shark migration pattern

■ Mako shark migration pattern

SHARKS AND HUMANS

Why Sharks Attack

Most shark attacks on humans happen for two reasons. First, sharks attack humans who are threatening them or being aggressive. Second, sharks attack when they think a human will make a good meal. A human is 16.5 times more likely to be hit by lightning than to be attacked by a shark.

HUMANS AT RISK

Most shark attacks occur close to shore, since that is where humans usually swim or surf. The great white shark (below) has been responsible for many attacks on humans.

DID YOU KNOW?

Great white sharks often attack from below, and for this reason sometimes mistake humans frolicking at the surface for prey.

79

Where Sharks Attack

Shark attacks have been recorded from Scotland to New Zealand. Most shark attacks happen nearer to the equator, where there are lots of sharks and lots of people. Many attacks have occurred in Australia, the United States, and South Africa—countries with long coastlines and seasonally warm temperatures. Because of this, people used to think that dangerous sharks prefer warm water. However, dangerous sharks are common in colder waters too; it is just that people are less inclined to join them.

SHARK ATTACK DISTRIBUTION
This map shows the relative worldwide distribution of authenticated cases of shark attack on humans that are recorded in the International Shark Attack File. The file contains a record of more than 3,000 investigations, from the mid-1500s to the present. However, it is possible that language barriers and other factors have resulted in the true number of attacks being understated in some areas.

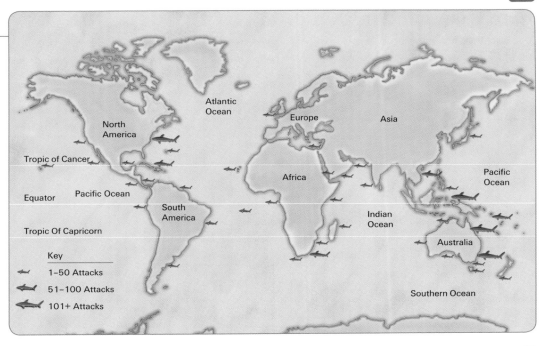

Atlantic
Ocean

North
America

Europe

Asia

Tropic of Cancer

Pacific
Ocean

Equator   Pacific Ocean

Africa

South
America

Indian
Ocean

Tropic Of Capricorn

Australia

Key

1–50 Attacks

51–100 Attacks

101+ Attacks

Southern Ocean

Taking Precautions

Shark attacks have prompted various responses, ranging from fencing off beaches to trying to eradicate the "problem." Some approaches focus on keeping sharks away from popular beaches; others aim to protect people in the water.

HOW FAR FROM SHORE?

The figures in the diagram, based on 570 incidents, provide a breakdown of attacks according to each victim's distance from shore. The figures in brackets show what percentage of people swim at these distances, indicating that attack statistics tell us nearly as much about the habits of people as they do about those of sharks.

BEACH NETTING

The illustrations show how nets are placed and secured to keep sharks out of popular swimming areas. Each end of a 500-foot (150-meter) net is secured by an anchor and its position is marked by floats, which also help to hold the net upright. The loosely hanging nets, about 20 feet (6 m) deep, are set in the late afternoon and usually hauled in the next morning.

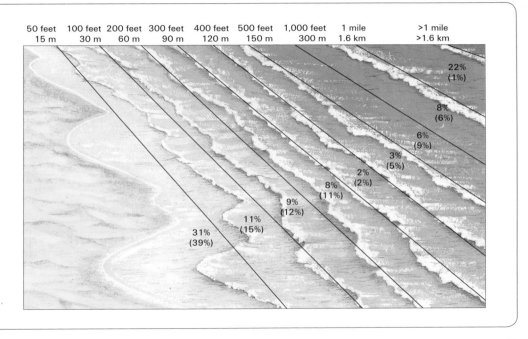

| 50 feet | 100 feet | 200 feet | 300 feet | 400 feet | 500 feet | 1,000 feet | 1 mile | >1 mile |
| 15 m | 30 m | 60 m | 90 m | 120 m | 150 m | 300 m | 1.6 km | >1.6 km |

22%
(1%)

8%
(6%)

6%
(9%)

3%
(5%)

2%
(2%)

8%
(11%)

9%
(12%)

11%
(15%)

31%
(39%)

Sharks as Resources

Humans have many uses for sharks. Shark meat is often eaten or used for fertilizer, and shark fins are made into soup. Oil rich in Vitamin A is taken from their livers, and chemicals used to thin human blood are extracted from their blood. Their eyes provide corneas for transplants, and their cartilage has medical uses. A shark has likely provided meat for our tables, lubricant for our machines, fertilizer for our plants—even oil for makeup.

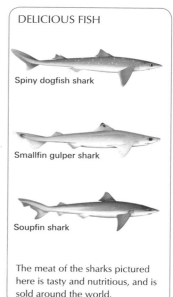

DELICIOUS FISH

Spiny dogfish shark

Smallfin gulper shark

Soupfin shark

The meat of the sharks pictured here is tasty and nutritious, and is sold around the world.

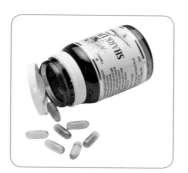

VALUABLE OIL
Shark liver oil, once prized as a lubricant and source of Vitamin A, has long been popular in Asia, renown for its healing properties. It is becoming more common in Western societies.

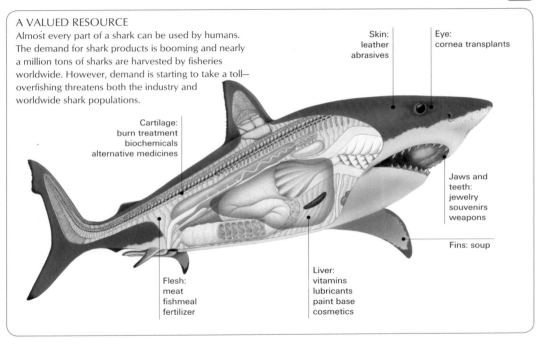

A VALUED RESOURCE

Almost every part of a shark can be used by humans. The demand for shark products is booming and nearly a million tons of sharks are harvested by fisheries worldwide. However, demand is starting to take a toll—overfishing threatens both the industry and worldwide shark populations.

Skin:
leather
abrasives

Eye:
cornea transplants

Cartilage:
burn treatment
biochemicals
alternative medicines

Jaws and
teeth:
jewelry
souvenirs
weapons

Fins: soup

Flesh:
meat
fishmeal
fertilizer

Liver:
vitamins
lubricants
paint base
cosmetics

Fishing for Sharks

Twelve million sharks are killed by humans each year, compared to the six humans killed annually by sharks. Because sharks are a top predator in the ocean, they are very important in maintaining the populations of many ocean animals. Overfishing of sharks will have serious consequences for the health of the whole ocean and all the people who depend on it.

FINS TO MARKET
Shark fins (seen drying right) have become very valuable because they are the key ingredient in popular shark fin soup. They are harvested worldwide and sold in Asia.

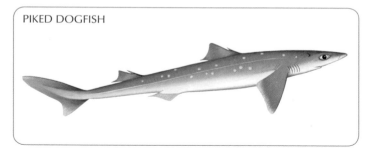

PIKED DOGFISH

SUPPORTING AN INDUSTRY
Dogfishes are small to medium-sized sharks that are essential to the global fishing industry, used for food and other products. The piked dogfish, possibly the world's most abundant shark, is a popular catch.

Threats to Sharks

In the past few decades, the human demand for sharks has increased greatly. Fishing is the greatest threat facing shark populations. Even if people stopped catching sharks on purpose, too many would still be accidentally caught and killed in nets cast for other fish. With some species facing extinction due to overfishing, scientists and fishers are trying to find ways to protect shark populations.

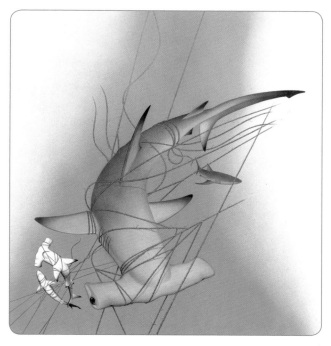

UNNECESSARY DEATHS
An adult and two baby hammerhead sharks are caught in a fishing net. Hammerheads can become trapped in nets along coastal waters.

ENVIRONMENTAL THREAT

Pollution from oil spills and industrial waste are threatening some shark populations, particularly in sheltered bays that sharks use to hatch young.

Sharks in Captivity

Sharks have been kept in aquariums since the late 1800s. Not long ago, people didn't care too much if a shark died in captivity. It was easier to replace a shark than to keep it alive, so they were caught, displayed, and then replaced when they died. These days, great care is taken to make sure sharks stay healthy and well fed in aquariums.

BIGGER AND BETTER
Because aquariums have learned more about caring for sharks, they can now make healthy homes for larger species, like the whale shark (right).

IN THE WILD
Few people ever get to see a shark in the wild. Most people would never see a shark if it weren't for aquariums.

Studying Sharks

Until the last few decades, most of what we knew about sharks we learned from studying deceased specimens. By dissecting dead sharks, scientists were able to determine their internal anatomy, the structure of their skeletons and sensory systems, their diet, their method of tooth replacement, and their various ways of reproducing.

DEEP-SEA RESEARCH
Observing sharks in the wild can be difficult and dangerous, but it makes a significant contribution to understanding how they live.

THICK-SKINNED
Because most sharks are large, and their skin is thick and quick to heal, it is easy and painless for them to be fitted with transmitters and tags so that they can be tracked and monitored over time.

OBSERVING SHARKS

In the Field

Responsible divers plan very carefully before swimming out to see sharks in the wild. Divers must be cautious not to damage sensitive ocean environments, and of course they must be very careful about their own safety around these sometimes dangerous animals!

BLUE THRILL
Each year, more and more people go out scuba diving to see sharks in the wild. This scuba diver (right) is swimming with a potentially dangerous blue shark.

SAFETY CLUES
Good divers look for safety clues in the environment. The behavior of other marine creatures can help divers know whether nearby sharks are agitated or calm.

Photographing Sharks

Now that waterproof cameras are common and affordable, many divers are eager to take pictures of their encounters with sharks. In addition, new camera technology has helped photographers get good footage at deep, dark depths. But undersea photographers have a lot to think about. They must not damage reefs with their flippers, blind sharks with their camera flashes, or get so wrapped up in their photography that they don't see danger coming.

READY FOR ITS CLOSE-UP
Protected by a steel cage, a diver is able to capture clear video footage of a great white shark in its natural habitat.

SAFETY FIRST
Divers need to be very careful when filming any large shark. They must be careful never to "corner" a shark against rocks or reefs, and to leave space for the shark to swim away.

A Shark Observer's Guide

You can venture all over the world to watch sharks in their natural habitats. Sharks only visit some of these places during part of the year, so plan ahead if you're going to visit.

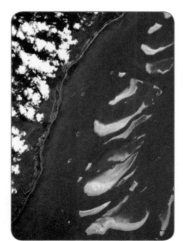

GREAT BARRIER REEF
The Great Barrier Reef, off the northeast coast of Australia, is the only living thing that can be seen from space. At Scuba Zoo, at Flinders Reef in the Coral Sea, caged divers can interact with and photograph gray reef, whitetip reef, and silvertip sharks.

SHARK-VIEWING SITES
1 San Diego, USA
2 Kona Coast, USA
3 Sea of Cortez, Mexico
4 Revillagigedo Islands, Mexico
5 Cocos Island, Costa Rica
6 The Bahamas
7 Galapagos Islands, Ecuador
8 Isle of Man, UK
9 Ras Muhammad, Egypt
10 Cape Town, South Africa
11 Similan and Surin Islands, Thailand
12 Yap and Palau, Micronesia
13 Rangiroa Atoll, French Polynesia
14 Mamanuca Islands, Fiji
15 Valeries Reef, Papua New Guinea
16 Ningaloo Reef, Australia
17 Neptune Islands, Australia
18 Great Barrier Reef, Australia
19 New South Wales, Australia
20 Lord Howe Island, Australia

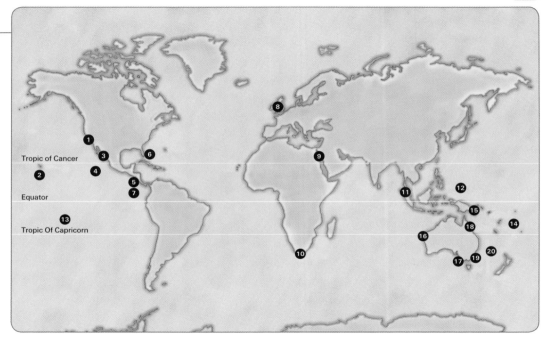

Tropic of Cancer

Equator

Tropic Of Capricorn

KINDS OF SHARKS

FRILLED SHARK

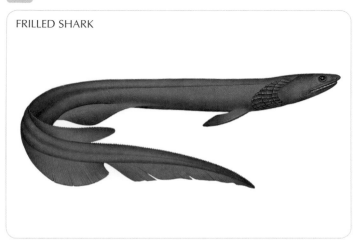

Key Facts

male and female 6.5 feet (2 m)

Other names: Frill-gilled shark, eel shark
Size at birth: 16 inches (40 cm)
Maximum length: 6.5 feet (2 m)
Diet: Other sharks, squid, and fishes
Habitat: Near the coasts of continents and islands, usually at depths between 400 and 4,200 feet (120–1,280 m)
Distribution: Wide-ranging but patchy in all oceans except northwestern Atlantic coast

The frilled shark is often called a living fossil because it looks so much like the early sharks of the Paleozoic Era. It lives deep in the ocean and is rarely seen by humans. However, sick or dying frilled sharks are sometimes sighted at the surface. It has an eel-like body and frilled gills that circle its neck, like a collar.

BLUNTNOSE SIXGILL SHARK

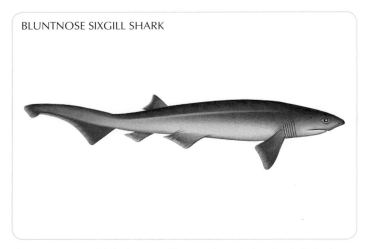

Key Facts

male and female 15.75 feet (4.8 m)

Other names: Sixgill shark, bull shark

Size at birth: 24–28 inches (60–70 cm)

Maximum length: 15.75 feet (4.8 m)

Diet: Wide-ranging, including other sharks, rays, bottom fishes, and even crabs and seals

Habitat: Shelves and slopes from the surface to 6,500 feet (2,000 m)

Distribution: Coastal, worldwide including oceanic islands

This massive, powerful shark is one of four species with six pairs of gill slits (most sharks have five pairs). It uses its long tail to swim in a strong, constant motion. It is a common species, most often seen at night. The bluntnose sixgill is a voracious predator of other large fishes and is fished for its meat and oil.

BROADNOSE SEVENGILL SHARK

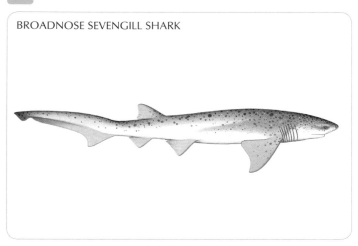

female 8 feet (2.4 m)

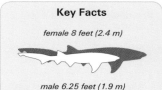

male 6.25 feet (1.9 m)

Other names: Cow shark, groundshark

Size at birth: 16–18 inches (40–45 cm)

Maximum length: 10 feet (3 m)

Diet: Wide-ranging, including other sharks, rays, bottom fishes, and seals

Habitat: Shallow bays and estuaries along the continental shelf as deep as 450 feet (135 m)

Distribution: Temperate coastal shelves, except for northern Atlantic

This shark is recognized by its seven pairs of gill slits—two more pairs than most sharks have. It will often come inshore in shallow bays and inlets, but does not rest on the seabed. This may explain why it is not commonly seen by divers. There are few records of it attacking people, but it will scavenge on human corpses. It is potentially dangerous and should be treated with caution.

BRAMBLE SHARK

Key Facts

female 7.25 feet (2.2 m)

male 5.25 feet (1.6 m)

Other names: Spinous shark, mango-tara

Size at birth: 1–3 feet (30–90 cm)

Maximum length: 10 feet (3 m)

Diet: Smaller sharks, fishes, and crabs

Habitat: Continental shelves and upper slopes, from 1,300 to 3,000 feet (400–900 m)

Distribution: Western Atlantic from Massachusetts to Virginia; Argentina; eastern Atlantic from North Sea to Mediterranean and southern Africa; India; New Zealand; southern Australia; Japan

The bramble shark gets its name from its prominent spine-like denticles, which are cone-shaped, pointy projections about a half inch (1.25 cm) in diameter at the base. They are scattered over the shark's body and on the underside of the snout. This fairly common, widespread species is often encountered in the Mediterranean Sea and along the west coasts of Europe and Africa.

PIKED DOGFISH

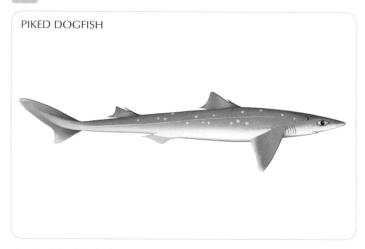

Key Facts

female 3.25 feet (100 cm)

male 2.5 feet (80 cm)

Other names: Spiny dogfish, skittledog, white-spotted dogfish, spotted spiny dogfish, spurdog, Victorian spotted dogfish, codshark, thornshark

Size at birth: 8–12 inches (20–30 cm)

Maximum length: 5 feet (1.5 m)

Diet: Small fishes, krill, and squid

Habitat: Coastal, from very shallow water to 2,600 feet (800 m)

Distribution: Atlantic and Pacific oceans; southwest Australia; tip of Africa

The piked dogfish, also known as the spiny dogfish, may be the world's most abundant shark. Even still, since it grows slowly and has few babies, it is vulnerable to overfishing and has disappeared in some areas. These sharks form huge schools that live in the shallow, coastal waters of higher latitudes in spring and fall. In the winter, they migrate into deep waters.

SMALLFIN GULPER DOGFISH

Key Facts

female 39 inches (98 cm)

male 34 inches (86 cm)

Other names: Endeavor dogfish, arrowspine dogfish

Size at birth: 12–15 inches (30–38 cm)

Maximum length: 39 inches (99 cm)

Diet: Oily and bottom fishes, small dogfish sharks, squid, octopuses, shrimp, and sea squirts

Habitat: The outer continental shelves and upper slopes at depths of 420–2,700 feet (130–820 m)

Distribution: Indo-West Pacific; scattered records from eastern South Africa eastward to Australia and Japan

One of fourteen members of the family known collectively as gulper dogfishes, the smallfin gulper dogfish is a common deepwater shark in some parts of its range. However, its numbers have been significantly depleted in recent years as a result of overharvesting. Along with numerous other species of dogfish sharks, it is much sought after for its meat and oil.

BLACKBELLY LANTERNSHARK

Key Facts

male 13.75 inches (35 cm)

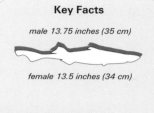

female 13.5 inches (34 cm)

Other names: Lucifer shark
Size at birth: 6 inches (15 cm)
Maximum length: 18 inches (45 cm)
Diet: Squid, shrimp, and small fishes
Habitat: Along slopes and shelves at depths of 590–3,300 feet (180–1,000 m)

Distribution: Southern and eastern Australia; New Zealand; China Sea to Japan

The lanternshark's name comes from the bioluminescent organs that run along its belly. These organs provide effective camouflage, making just enough glowing light to equal the amount of filtered-down light between them and the ocean's surface. Because of this optical illusion, they merge with the ocean and cannot be seen by potential predators—or by unsuspecting prey.

GREENLAND SLEEPER SHARK

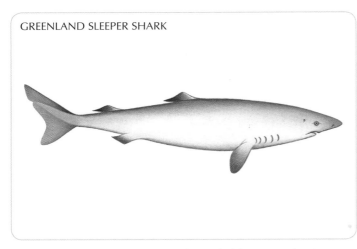

Key Facts

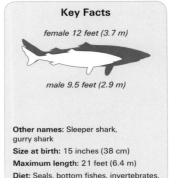

female 12 feet (3.7 m)

male 9.5 feet (2.9 m)

Other names: Sleeper shark, gurry shark
Size at birth: 15 inches (38 cm)
Maximum length: 21 feet (6.4 m)
Diet: Seals, bottom fishes, invertebrates, and carrion
Habitat: From shallow water to 1,800 feet (550 m)
Distribution: North Atlantic Ocean

The only polar shark of the Atlantic, this sleeper shark lives in near-freezing water at depths of up to 1,800 feet (550 m). It rises to more shallow water only in the colder months. At such depths and temperatures, it is not seen by divers, although it has been caught by fishers. It got its name because it moves very slowly and doesn't fight much when caught by fishermen.

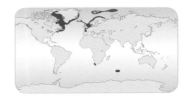

PRICKLY DOGFISH

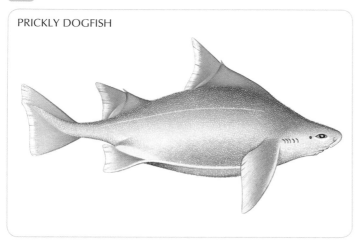

Key Facts

female 2.5 feet (75 cm)

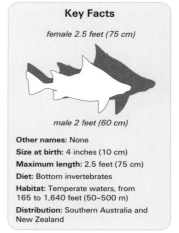

male 2 feet (60 cm)

Other names: None
Size at birth: 4 inches (10 cm)
Maximum length: 2.5 feet (75 cm)
Diet: Bottom invertebrates
Habitat: Temperate waters, from 165 to 1,640 feet (50–500 m)
Distribution: Southern Australia and New Zealand

This odd-looking and rarely seen shark gets its name from its cover of short, spiny denticles. It is triangle-shaped with a flattish head and unusually large, sail-like dorsal fins, each with a single sharp spike. Its mouth looks somewhat like that of the cookiecutter shark. It is sluggish and not known to be dangerous to humans.

COOKIECUTTER SHARK

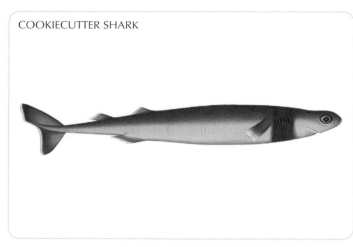

Key Facts

female 20 inches (50 cm)

male 16 inches (40 cm)

Other names: Cigar shark, luminous shark

Size at birth: Unknown

Maximum length: 20 inches (50 cm)

Diet: Squid, and pieces of large fishes and marine animals

Habitat: Oceanic, migrating from depths of 3,300 feet (1,000 m) to the surface each night

Distribution: Widespread, mostly oceanic

Before its feeding behavior was discovered, this species was called the cigar shark. The more recent name arises from its distinctive teeth, jaws, and lips, which allow this shark to form a suction cup on its prey's skin, bite down, and then swivel to cut out a circular plug of tissue—like a cookiecutter in pastry.

SPINED PYGMY SHARK

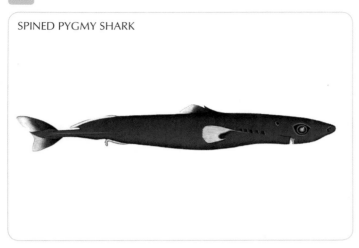

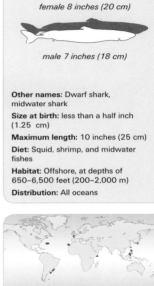

Key Facts

female 8 inches (20 cm)

male 7 inches (18 cm)

Other names: Dwarf shark, midwater shark

Size at birth: less than a half inch (1.25 cm)

Maximum length: 10 inches (25 cm)

Diet: Squid, shrimp, and midwater fishes

Habitat: Offshore, at depths of 650–6,500 feet (200–2,000 m)

Distribution: All oceans

This tiny, widespread shark lives in the cold depths of temperate and tropical waters, near continents and islands. Like other deepwater sharks, it makes a daily migration to feed. It rises at dusk, stopping within 650 feet (200 m) of the surface, and feeds on squid, shrimp, and midwater fishes. The bioluminescent photophores on its underside camouflage it. At dawn, it descends to rest.

LONGNOSE SAWSHARK

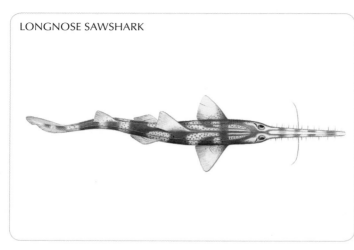

Key Facts

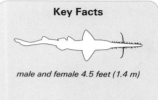

male and female 4.5 feet (1.4 m)

Other names: Common sawshark
Size at birth: 11–15 inches (27–38 cm)
Maximum length: 4.5 feet (1.4 m)
Diet: Small bony fishes
Habitat: Continental shelves and slopes to about 1,000 feet (300 m)
Distribution: Southern Australia

Although most sawsharks are present in the Atlantic, Pacific, and Indian oceans, this species is only found along the coasts of southern Australia. It is a timid and generally harmless species, but may lash out with its powerful snout if handled. It feeds by trailing its antennae-like barbels along the seafloor to locate small fish. The teeth on the snout then stir up sand to rouse the prey.

115

PACIFIC ANGELSHARK

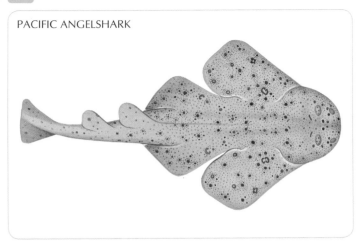

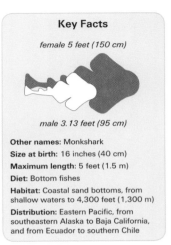

Key Facts

female 5 feet (150 cm)

male 3.13 feet (95 cm)

Other names: Monkshark
Size at birth: 16 inches (40 cm)
Maximum length: 5 feet (1.5 m)
Diet: Bottom fishes
Habitat: Coastal sand bottoms, from shallow waters to 4,300 feet (1,300 m)
Distribution: Eastern Pacific, from southeastern Alaska to Baja California, and from Ecuador to southern Chile

This shark is also known as the monkshark because its head was thought to resemble the hood of a monk's cloak. The Pacific angelshark spends its day buried in sand, with only its eyes and head exposed. In this position it is ready to seize hold of an unsuspecting fish in its large jaws and spiky teeth. It was once common but its numbers have been reduced as a result of heavy fishing.

HORN SHARK

Key Facts

male 25 inches (64 cm)

female 23 inches (58 cm)

Other names: Bullhead shark, Californian horn shark

Size at birth: 6 inches (15 cm)

Maximum length: 4 feet (1.2 m) but rarely larger than 3 feet (1 m)

Diet: Sea urchins, crustaceans, and small fish

Habitat: Among large rocks at the base of kelp beds

Distribution: Central California to Baja California

The horn shark is named for the spine in front of each of its dorsal fins. Part of its scientific name, *Heterodontus* (from Greek for "mixed-tooth"), refers to the pointed teeth at the front of these sharks' jaws and the blunt teeth at the rear. With these versatile teeth, they are well equipped to devour a variety of tasty sea creatures. They also use their large pectoral fins to "walk" on the seafloor.

117

NECKLACE CARPETSHARK

Key Facts

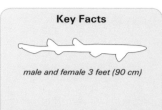

male and female 3 feet (90 cm)

Other names: Varied carpetshark, southern carpetshark, varied catshark
Size at birth: Unknown
Maximum length: 3 feet (90 cm)
Diet: Unknown, however its teeth suggest crustaceans
Habitat: Continental shelves to 1,600 feet (500 m)
Distribution: Southwestern Australia to southern Australia

The necklace carpetshark, which is found only in southern Australian waters, is active at night, when it is sometimes encountered by divers. During the day it is difficult to spot because it rests in caves or on the sandy bottom, where it is perfectly camouflaged by its multicolored patterning.

BLIND SHARK

Key Facts

male and female 4 feet (1.2 m)

Other names: Brown catshark
Size at birth: 7 inches (18 cm)
Maximum length: 4 feet (1.2 m)
Diet: Reef fish and invertebrates
Habitat: Rocky shores from tide pools to 330 feet (100 m)
Distribution: Central eastern Australia

Despite its name, this harmless species is not blind. It appears to be because it rotates its eyeballs backward when frightened (such as when it is taken from the water). The blind shark is nocturnal, sheltering under ledges and in caves during the day and emerging at night to forage on the reef and in the sand.

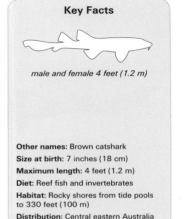

ORNATE WOBBEGONG

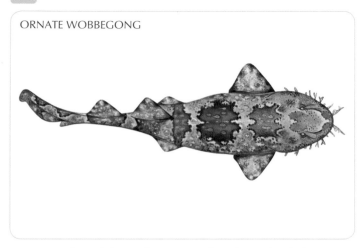

Key Facts

male and female 9.5 feet (2.9 m)

Other names: Banded wobbegong, carpetshark, gulf wobbegong

Size at birth: 8 inches (20 cm)

Maximum length: 9.5 feet (2.9 m)

Diet: Bottom invertebrates and bony fishes

Habitat: Inshore, from shallow water to 330 feet (100 m)

Distribution: Papua New Guinea; eastern, southern and southwestern Australia

A common inshore inhabitant of temperate rocky and tropical reefs, the ornate wobbegong rests during the day on rocky bottoms or coral, where it is perfectly camouflaged by its markings and irregular frills. It becomes active at night, searching for invertebrates and fishes. Twenty-three attacks have been documented in Australian waters from encounters with divers and fishers.

EPAULETTE SHARK

male and female 3.5 feet (107 cm)

Other names: Ocellated bambooshark
Size at birth: 6 inches (15 cm)
Maximum length: 3.5 feet (107 cm)
Diet: Invertebrates
Habitat: Shallow inshore reefs
Distribution: New Guinea; northwest to northeastern Australia

The epaulette shark is one of twelve described species of longtailed carpetshark. Most of these sharks are small, with thin, slightly flattened, elongated bodies. The epaulette shark is reasonably common within its range. Divers often encounter adults resting during the day, but juveniles are rarely seen, as they hide within the coral or rocky reefs, which are their principal habitats.

ZEBRA SHARK

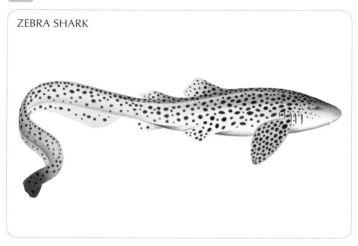

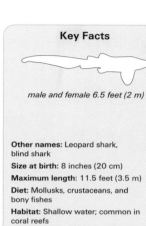

male and female 6.5 feet (2 m)

Other names: Leopard shark, blind shark

Size at birth: 8 inches (20 cm)

Maximum length: 11.5 feet (3.5 m)

Diet: Mollusks, crustaceans, and bony fishes

Habitat: Shallow water; common in coral reefs

Distribution: Tropical western Pacific and Indian oceans to eastern Africa

When young, this shark is covered with stripes that look like those of a zebra, which is why it is called a zebra shark. It is also known as the leopard shark because of the brown spots that develop on adult zebra sharks. Divers often see them resting on the seafloor, propped up on their pectoral fins, facing into the current with their mouths open to take in oxygen more easily from the water.

NURSE SHARK

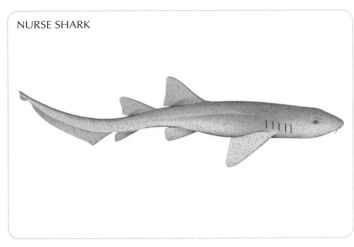

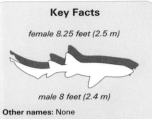
This shark may have been named after the noise made by a feeding nurse shark, which sounds like a nursing baby. Common over inshore reefs in tropical waters, the nurse shark is sluggish during the day, but active at night, when it feeds on bottom-dwelling fish. Because they are abundant, easy to capture, and adapt well to captivity, they are often seen in aquariums.

WHALE SHARK

Key Facts

male 29.5 feet (9 m)

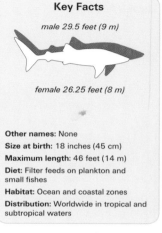

female 26.25 feet (8 m)

Other names: None
Size at birth: 18 inches (45 cm)
Maximum length: 46 feet (14 m)
Diet: Filter feeds on plankton and small fishes
Habitat: Ocean and coastal zones
Distribution: Worldwide in tropical and subtropical waters

The sole surviving member of its family, the whale shark is the world's largest living fish. This filter feeder swims slowly near the surface, consuming its prey, which can include fish as large as mackerel. It frequently enters tropical lagoons, where it mixes peacefully with snorkelers and divers.

GOBLIN SHARK

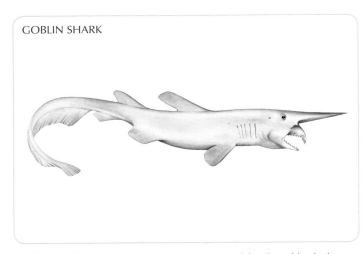

Key Facts

male and female 9.5 feet (2.9 m)

Other names: Elfin shark

Size at birth: Unknown

Maximum length: 12.75 feet (3.9 m)

Diet: Little is known; however, its fragile, pointed teeth indicate soft-bodied prey such as squid and shrimp

Habitat: Upper continental slope, near the bottom, at 1,180–1,800 feet (360–550 m)

Distribution: Scattered tropical and temperate locations in the Atlantic, Indian and Pacific oceans

Until it was rediscovered in the 1890s, it was assumed that the goblin shark, a sluggish bottom-dweller, had been extinct for 100 million years. It was known only from early specimens that had been preserved through the ages. Even today, little is understood about this deepwater shark.

SAND TIGER SHARK

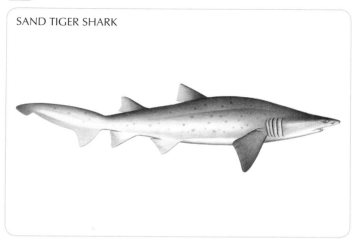

Key Facts

female 8.5 feet (2.6 m)

male 8 feet (2.4 m)

Other names: Gray nurse, sand shark, (spotted) raggedtooth shark

Size at birth: 3.25 feet (1 m)

Maximum length: 10.25 feet (3.2 m)

Diet: Fish, rays, crabs, and lobsters

Habitat: Coastal, from sandy beaches and reefs to 625 feet (190 m)

Distribution: Northwestern and eastern Atlantic; Gulf of Mexico; Argentina; southern Africa; Red Sea; Australia; Indonesia; China Sea to Sea of Japan

This large, fearsome-looking (but gentle) shark swims with its mouth open, exposing its long needle-like teeth. The sand tiger shark can hover motionlessly in the water by swallowing surface air and holding it in its stomach, achieving near-neutral buoyancy. It is known to make long migrations to reproduce. It lives in shallow bays and sandy coastal waters and on rocky or tropical reefs.

CROCODILE SHARK

Key Facts

female 3.13 feet (95 cm)

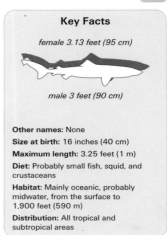

male 3 feet (90 cm)

Other names: None
Size at birth: 16 inches (40 cm)
Maximum length: 3.25 feet (1 m)
Diet: Probably small fish, squid, and crustaceans
Habitat: Mainly oceanic, probably midwater, from the surface to 1,900 feet (590 m)
Distribution: All tropical and subtropical areas

This muscular shark is widespread throughout tropical and subtropical waters and is also sometimes seen offshore. It is a fast-swimming predator that chases small prey, either near the surface or down to 1,000 feet (300 m) deep. With its powerful jaws and slender, sharp teeth, the crocodile shark is well equipped to seize hold of prey. However, it is not dangerous to humans.

THRESHER SHARK

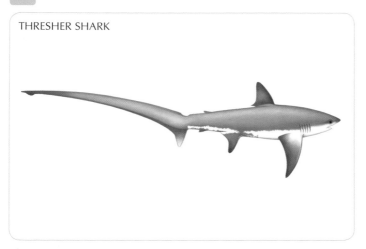

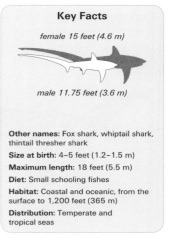
This shark is widespread in tropical and temperate waters and, although it often lives at considerable depths, it also swims at the surface of coastal waters. It frightens its prey and herds it into groups by slapping the water with its large tail, which it also uses to stun prey. It has been targeted by fisheries for its fins and meat; its numbers have decreased as a result of overfishing.

BASKING SHARK

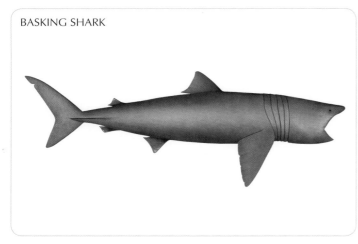

The basking shark is second in size only to the whale shark. This shark frequently visits temperate waters, where it takes advantage of seasonal plankton blooms. It often enters large bays and can be seen close to shore, swimming at the surface with its mouth open to form a huge "net." Water passes into the mouth and across the gill rakers, which strain out plankton.

GREAT WHITE SHARK

Key Facts

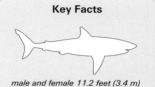

male and female 11.2 feet (3.4 m)

Other names: White shark, white death, white pointer, blue pointer

Size at birth: 3–4 feet (90–120 cm)

Maximum length: reports of 24 feet (7.3 m)

Diet: Seals, sea lions, dolphins, porpoises, sharks, carrion, seabirds, turtles, bony fishes, and invertebrates

Habitat: Coastal cooler waters, extending to tropics and open ocean

Distribution: Temperate waters

A star of film and literature, the great white is the most feared of sharks. It is responsible for most unprovoked attacks on humans. Despite this, many divers descend in steel cages to observe this superb predator at close range. It prefers shallow, cool, coastal waters, but is occasionally seen close to the equator. It hunts during the day for other sharks and marine mammals.

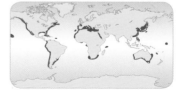

130

SHORTFIN MAKO

Key Facts

female 11 feet (3.4 m)

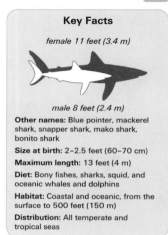

male 8 feet (2.4 m)

Other names: Blue pointer, mackerel shark, snapper shark, mako shark, bonito shark

Size at birth: 2–2.5 feet (60–70 cm)

Maximum length: 13 feet (4 m)

Diet: Bony fishes, sharks, squid, and oceanic whales and dolphins

Habitat: Coastal and oceanic, from the surface to 500 feet (150 m)

Distribution: All temperate and tropical seas

Ernest Hemingway's novel *The Old Man and the Sea* reinforced the shortfin mako's reputation as a fighting sport fish. This widely distributed and fastest moving of all the sharks uses its speed to bear down on and capture its prey. It is also a long-distance swimmer. One shortfin mako was tracked traveling 1,332 miles (2,128 km) in thirty-seven days, an average of 36 miles (58 km) a day.

PORBEAGLE SHARK

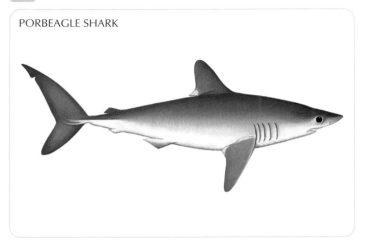

Key Facts

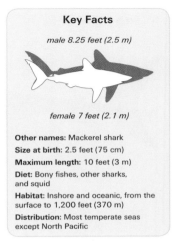

male 8.25 feet (2.5 m)

female 7 feet (2.1 m)

Other names: Mackerel shark
Size at birth: 2.5 feet (75 cm)
Maximum length: 10 feet (3 m)
Diet: Bony fishes, other sharks, and squid
Habitat: Inshore and oceanic, from the surface to 1,200 feet (370 m)
Distribution: Most temperate seas except North Pacific

This shark is extremely powerful and fast. It shares with its North Pacific relative, the salmon shark, the generic name *Lamna*. To the ancient Greeks, *lamna* signified "a horrible monster of man-eating tendencies," and it was invoked to frighten children. The salmon and porbeagle sharks resemble each other so closely that they were not recognized as separate species until 1947.

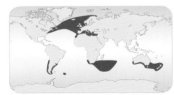

BROWN CATSHARK

Key Facts

male 21 inches (53 cm)

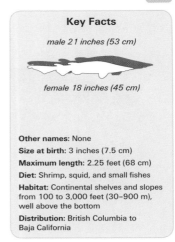

female 18 inches (45 cm)

Other names: None
Size at birth: 3 inches (7.5 cm)
Maximum length: 2.25 feet (68 cm)
Diet: Shrimp, squid, and small fishes
Habitat: Continental shelves and slopes from 100 to 3,000 feet (30–900 m), well above the bottom
Distribution: British Columbia to Baja California

Although the brown catshark is a common dweller along the west coast of North America, little is known about its lifestyle. Brown catsharks, who got their name from their cat-like eyes, seem to be fairly sluggish and sedentary and to move only short distances during their lives. Unlike other catshark species, this medium-sized deepwater shark does not live on the seafloor.

SWELLSHARK

Key Facts

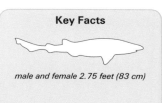

male and female 2.75 feet (83 cm)

Other names: None
Size at birth: 5.5 inches (14 cm)
Maximum length: 3.5 feet (1 m)
Diet: Bottom fish
Habitat: Beneath and around kelp beds near reefs, from depths of 30–200 feet (10–60 m)
Distribution: Temperate eastern Pacific, from California to Mexico and central Chile

One of the largest catsharks, the sluggish, nocturnal, and highly distinctive swellshark is impossible to mistake for any other shark. Swellsharks get their common name from their habit of swallowing water when threatened. In this way they can balloon themselves up to three times their normal size—until they become wedged inside a rock crevice and are safe from predators.

GRACEFUL CATSHARK

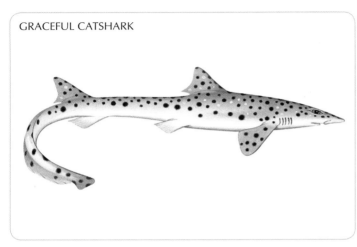

female 20 inches (50 cm)

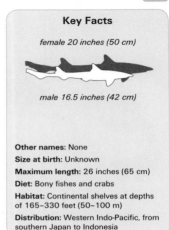

male 16.5 inches (42 cm)

Other names: None
Size at birth: Unknown
Maximum length: 26 inches (65 cm)
Diet: Bony fishes and crabs
Habitat: Continental shelves at depths of 165–330 feet (50–100 m)
Distribution: Western Indo-Pacific, from southern Japan to Indonesia

The graceful catshark is a species of finback catsharks. Finback catsharks are similar to true catsharks, except for the placement of their first dorsal fins, either in front of or above their pelvic fins. (True catsharks' dorsal fins lie behind their pelvic fins.) This shark is the only finback that lays eggs. It lives above island and continental shelves in warm temperate and tropical waters.

FALSE CATSHARK

Key Facts

female 8.25 feet (2.5 m)

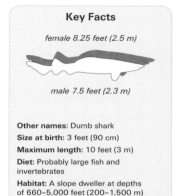

male 7.5 feet (2.3 m)

Other names: Dumb shark
Size at birth: 3 feet (90 cm)
Maximum length: 10 feet (3 m)
Diet: Probably large fish and invertebrates
Habitat: A slope dweller at depths of 660–5,000 feet (200–1,500 m)
Distribution: Patchy; in all tropical oceans and Hawaii and the North Atlantic

The false catshark is a large, slope-dwelling shark that lives mainly in cold waters. However, it has an uneven distribution that extends its range into some tropical waters. The false catshark's body is watery and soft, which may give it the neutral buoyancy that suits its sedentary lifestyle near the seafloor.

BARBELED HOUNDSHARK

Key Facts

female 28 inches (70 cm)

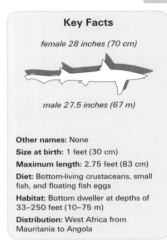

male 27.5 inches (67 m)

Other names: None

Size at birth: 1 feet (30 cm)

Maximum length: 2.75 feet (83 cm)

Diet: Bottom-living crustaceans, small fish, and floating fish eggs

Habitat: Bottom dweller at depths of 33–250 feet (10–75 m)

Distribution: West Africa from Mauritania to Angola

This small species prefers muddy bottom areas, especially near river mouths, where it feeds on small fishes, crustaceans, and squid. Males have larger teeth than females. They may use these to grasp the females during mating. The barbeled houndshark is fished in West Africa for its meat and its skin.

TOPE SHARK

Key Facts

female 5.25 feet (1.6 m)

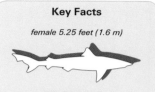

male 5 feet (1.5 m)

Other names: Soupfin shark, school shark, vitamin shark, snapper shark

Size at birth: 1 feet (30 cm)

Maximum length: 6.5 feet (2 m)

Diet: Mostly bony fishes, but also squid and octopus

Habitat: Coastal, on bottom from shallow water to 1,800 feet (550 m)

Distribution: Widespread in Pacific and Atlantic oceans, Mediterranean Sea, southern Australia and New Zealand

This long-lived shark, which has a potential lifespan of about sixty years, has been known to migrate long distances, probably to allow pregnant females to give birth in cooler waters. The tope shark is fished for its meat, fins, and liver oil. Its popularity among fishers, and the species' low reproduction rate, puts the tope shark population at risk of endangerment.

DUSKY SMOOTHHOUND

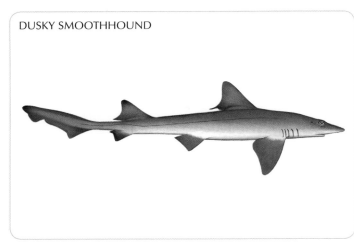

The dusky smoothhound lives mainly in temperate waters on continental shelves. Some dusky smoothhounds are also found on the continental slopes, as far as 1,900 feet (580 m) deep. It displays a preference for mud, sand, and rocky bottoms, commonly in enclosed bays. It never ventures into the open ocean. These sharks enter fresh water, but can't survive there for long.

LEOPARD SHARK

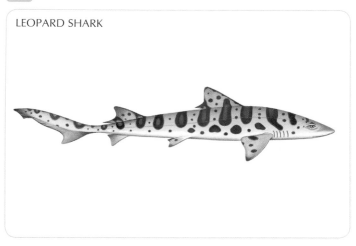

Key Facts

female 5 feet (1.5 m)

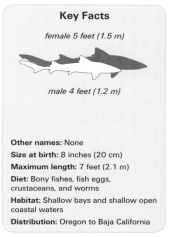

male 4 feet (1.2 m)

Other names: None
Size at birth: 8 inches (20 cm)
Maximum length: 7 feet (2.1 m)
Diet: Bony fishes, fish eggs,
crustaceans, and worms
Habitat: Shallow bays and shallow open
coastal waters
Distribution: Oregon to Baja California

The leopard shark is a regular inhabitant of bays along the coast of northern
California. It survives well in captivity and its attractive markings make it a popular
occupant of aquariums. Each year they migrate from the inner bays to the outer
coast of the Pacific Northwest. They are harmless to humans, but due to their
markings they are often mistaken for the dangerous tiger shark.

ATLANTIC WEASEL SHARK

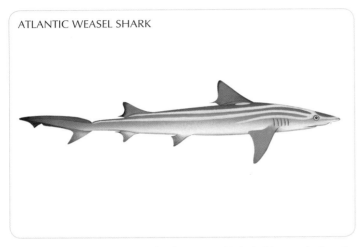

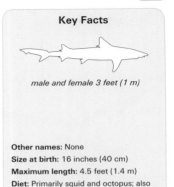

male and female 3 feet (1 m)

Other names: None

Size at birth: 16 inches (40 cm)

Maximum length: 4.5 feet (1.4 m)

Diet: Primarily squid and octopus; also small fish

Habitat: Shallow water to 330 feet (100 m)

Distribution: Tropical western Africa

The Atlantic weasel shark is immediately recognizable by its blue-gray body and yellow stripes. Its small range and limited distribution mean that, though it is easily recognizable by its distinctive markings, it is rarely sighted and, so far at least, only poorly understood. Like the other weasel sharks, it is an inshore species, living in shelf waters at modest depths along the coast of West Africa.

SILVERTIP SHARK

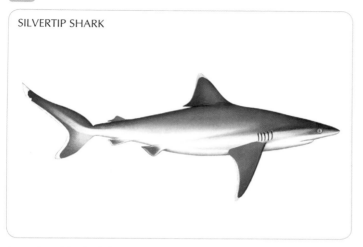

Key Facts

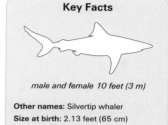

male and female 10 feet (3 m)

Other names: Silvertip whaler

Size at birth: 2.13 feet (65 cm)

Maximum length: 10 feet (3 m)

Diet: Bottom fishes

Habitat: Along reef drop-offs from the surface to 2,625 feet (800 m)

Distribution: Widespread in tropical Indo-Pacific; east coast of Africa from the Red Sea and South Africa eastward to the eastern Pacific; Mexico to Colombia

A member of the family known as requiem sharks, the silvertip gets its name from the white tips on its fins. Silvertip sharks prefer offshore islands and coral reefs, and adults typically inhabit waters below 82 feet (25 m). However, they also often enter lagoons, where they are most often encountered. These large sharks are known to sometimes harass divers, but they rarely attack.

GRAY REEF SHARK

Key Facts

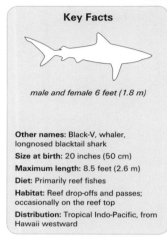

male and female 6 feet (1.8 m)

Other names: Black-V, whaler, longnosed blacktail shark

Size at birth: 20 inches (50 cm)

Maximum length: 8.5 feet (2.6 m)

Diet: Primarily reef fishes

Habitat: Reef drop-offs and passes; occasionally on the reef top

Distribution: Tropical Indo-Pacific, from Hawaii westward

One of the requiem sharks, the gray reef shark is among the most common sharks on Indo-Pacific coral reefs. An inquisitive and dangerous shark, it is attracted to the low-frequency underwater sounds made by a speared fish and will often take fishes off spearfishers' spears! Attacks are preceded by a warning display that involves head wagging, lowered pectoral fins, and an arched back.

GALAPAGOS SHARK

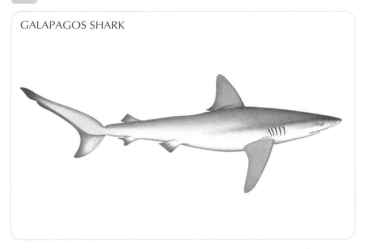

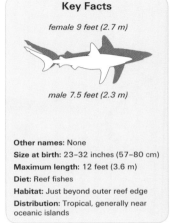

Key Facts

female 9 feet (2.7 m)

male 7.5 feet (2.3 m)

Other names: None
Size at birth: 23–32 inches (57–80 cm)
Maximum length: 12 feet (3.6 m)
Diet: Reef fishes
Habitat: Just beyond outer reef edge
Distribution: Tropical, generally near oceanic islands

This large, grayish requiem shark was named in 1905 after specimens found in the waters of the Galapagos Islands. It can be seen beyond the reef edge of tropical islands, either near the surface or near the bottom. It feeds on bottom-dwelling fish, squid, and octopus. This aggressive shark does not normally attack humans, but fatal attacks against swimmers have been recorded.

BULL SHARK

Key Facts

female 8 feet (2.4 m)

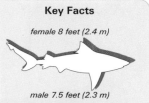

male 7.5 feet (2.3 m)

Other names: Lake Nicaragua shark, freshwater whaler, Zambezi shark

Size at birth: 22–32 inches (55–80 cm)

Maximum length: 11.5 feet (3.5 m)

Diet: Omnivorous: turtles, birds, dolphins, crustaceans, cephalopods, but prefers bony fishes and other sharks

Habitat: Estuaries, rivers and coastal waters to 100 feet (30 m)

Distribution: All tropical and sub-tropical seas

This large, sluggish gray shark is widespread along continental coasts. It also enters rivers and lakes. The bull shark can tolerate both highly salty sea water and fresh water, and has been recorded far up the Mississippi and Amazon rivers. It will eat almost anything it can capture. It is, perhaps, the most lethal of all sharks, and will attack humans. It lives and hunts alone.

145

OCEANIC WHITETIP SHARK

Key Facts

female 7.5 feet (2.3 m)

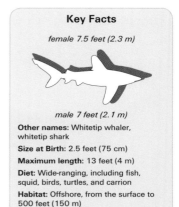

male 7 feet (2.1 m)

Other names: Whitetip whaler, whitetip shark

Size at Birth: 2.5 feet (75 cm)

Maximum length: 13 feet (4 m)

Diet: Wide-ranging, including fish, squid, birds, turtles, and carrion

Habitat: Offshore, from the surface to 500 feet (150 m)

Distribution: All tropical and subtropical seas

This large requiem shark is usually found far offshore. In the open ocean it can often be seen from boats or encountered by divers. It is most abundant in the tropics, but can also be found from southern California to southern Australia, following the warm water masses. It will eat almost anything it can find in the open sea, including whale carcasses and garbage dumped from ships.

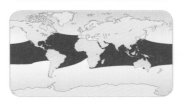

BLACKTIP REEF SHARK

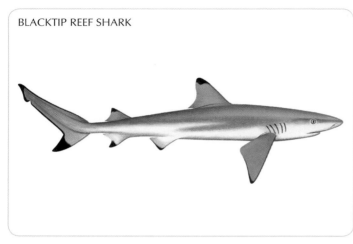

Key Facts

male 4.66 feet (1.4 m)

female 3.66 feet (1.1 m)

Other names: Blacktip shark, guliman

Size at birth: 20 inches (50 cm)

Maximum length: 6 feet (1.8 m)

Diet: Primarily reef fish, but also crustaceans, squid, and octopus

Habitat: Shallow reef flats to outer reef edge

Distribution: Tropical central Pacific to eastern Africa; entered the Mediterranean through Suez Canal

Blacktip reef sharks are among the most common sharks in the lagoons and coral reefs of the tropical Pacific and Indian oceans. Divers and snorkelers often see these sharks patrolling in shallow waters from about 1 foot (30 cm) deep. Because they are a small species, a number of these sharks have been captured in the central Pacific, and sent to aquariums worldwide.

TIGER SHARK

Key Facts

female 12 feet (3.7 m)

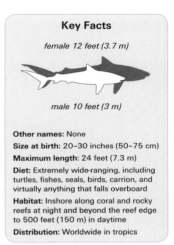

male 10 feet (3 m)

Other names: None

Size at birth: 20–30 inches (50–75 cm)

Maximum length: 24 feet (7.3 m)

Diet: Extremely wide-ranging, including turtles, fishes, seals, birds, carrion, and virtually anything that falls overboard

Habitat: Inshore along coral and rocky reefs at night and beyond the reef edge to 500 feet (150 m) in daytime

Distribution: Worldwide in tropics

One of the few true shark scavengers, this large, dangerous shark has eaten cattle, pigs, donkeys, sheep, and humans that have fallen overboard. Adult tiger sharks spend most of their days beyond the reef edge. They are active at night, and enter shallow reefs and lagoons to feed. They migrate between islands to take advantage of colonies of young birds learning to fly over water.

LEMON SHARK

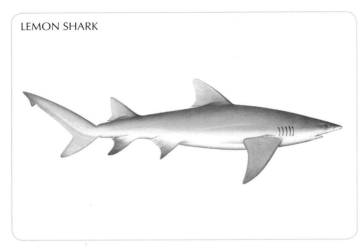

Key Facts

female 8.5 feet (2.6 m)

male 8.25 feet (2.5 m)

Other names: None

Size at birth: 2 feet (60 cm)

Maximum length: 11 feet (3.4 m)

Diet: Bony fish, rays, crustaceans, and mollusks

Habitat: Shallow sea grass beds and mangrove flats

Distribution: Western Atlantic from New Jersey to Brazil; possibly eastern Atlantic; eastern Pacific from Baja California to Ecuador

This shark is abundant in tropical reef systems, especially those with sea grass and mangrove habitats. Lemon sharks are active throughout the day and night. Some populations seem to undertake long migrations in search of food, because they are found in the summer months along continental shelves and sandy beaches in areas of high latitude. It survives well in captivity.

BLUE SHARK

Key Facts

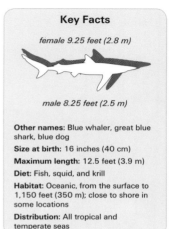

female 9.25 feet (2.8 m)

male 8.25 feet (2.5 m)

Other names: Blue whaler, great blue shark, blue dog
Size at birth: 16 inches (40 cm)
Maximum length: 12.5 feet (3.9 m)
Diet: Fish, squid, and krill
Habitat: Oceanic, from the surface to 1,150 feet (350 m); close to shore in some locations
Distribution: All tropical and temperate seas

One of the most attractive sharks, the blue shark is found in the open ocean throughout the tropics and cooler seas. In the tropics it often enters deeper, cooler water, while in temperate coastal waters it comes close to the edge of kelp beds. Once the most plentiful shark in the sea, it is now endangered due to overfishing. It will attack humans without being provoked.

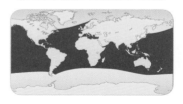

WHITETIP REEF SHARK

Key Facts

female 4.5 feet (1.4 m)

male 4.25 feet (1.3 m)

Other names: Blunthead shark
Size at birth: 21–24 inches (52–60 cm)
Maximum length: 7 feet (2.1 m)
Diet: Bottom fish, crustaceans, and squid
Habitat: A shallow-water reef dweller, to depths of 1,000 feet (300 m)
Distribution: Tropical eastern Pacific to eastern Africa; widespread in Oceania

These sluggish, slender requiem sharks live close to shore. During the day, they often rest in caves, particularly in Hawaii and the Galapagos Islands. They are active at night and during slack tides. They can become accustomed to the sounds of boats, and often approach divers out of curiosity. They are not aggressive to humans, but these sharks should be approached with caution.

SCALLOPED HAMMERHEAD SHARK

Key Facts

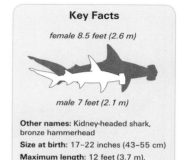

female 8.5 feet (2.6 m)

male 7 feet (2.1 m)

Other names: Kidney-headed shark, bronze hammerhead

Size at birth: 17–22 inches (43–55 cm)

Maximum length: 12 feet (3.7 m), possibly larger

Diet: Bony fish and squid

Habitat: Coastal, from the surface to 900 feet (270 m)

Distribution: Worldwide in tropical and warm-temperate seas

This large, active shark has a wide, hammer-like head that adds lift during swimming. Its eyes are located at the tips of its head, helping it capture elusive prey. This shark lives in coastal areas above continental and island shelves and the nearby offshore waters. Divers often spot them interacting playfully in shallow bays—frolicking, shaking their heads, and biting each other.

GREAT HAMMERHEAD SHARK

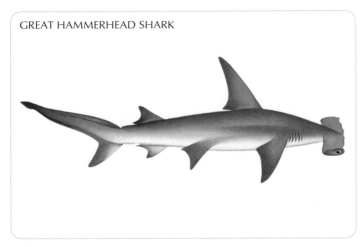

Key Facts

female 12 feet (3.7 m)

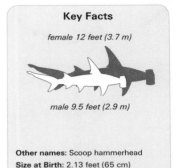

male 9.5 feet (2.9 m)

Other names: Scoop hammerhead
Size at Birth: 2.13 feet (65 cm)
Maximum length: 20 feet (6.1 m)
Diet: Other sharks and rays
Habitat: Coastal and above continental shelves, from surface to 260 feet (80 m)
Distribution: All tropical seas

The great hammerhead is an impressive predator. Its diet consists of many mobile fishes such as grouper and flatfishes. But it is best known as a hunter of stingrays, skates, and other sharks. Divers are likely to see this species in shallow waters, especially near coral reef drop-offs and adjacent sand habitats. It makes long migrations to cooler waters during the summer.

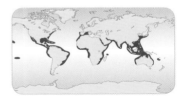

Glossary

bioluminescence The ability of some deep-sea creatures to make their own light in the dark ocean, using organs called photophores.

bottom-dweller A shark that spends most of its time on the ocean floor.

camouflage Colors and patterns on a shark that help it blend in with its natural surroundings.

captivity Any place a shark is kept after it is taken from its habitat.

cartilage The hard but flexible tissue that makes up the skeletons of sharks, rays, and chimaeras.

caudal fin The powerful tail that sharks use to move in the water.

Cenozoic Era The era when more mammal species appeared, starting about 65 million years ago.

chimera A shark relative that mainly lives on the ocean floor.

Cladoselache An extinct ancestor to the shark that lived during the Devonian Period.

denticles Small, cone-shaped scales that cover sharks' skin, giving it a sandpapery texture.

Devonian Period The era when the first sharks evolved, about 400 million years ago.

dorsal fin The fins on sharks' backs that help them maintain balance and control the speed and direction of their movements.

electrosense The sense that allows sharks to feel water movements and detect when prey or predators are close.

filter feeder An animal that feeds on tiny particles in the water.

gill filaments The parts of gills that filter oxygen to the blood.

lateral line Sensitive tubes inside the shark's body that detect vibrations and the small electric fields made by prey in the water.

netting Placing large nets underwater to keep sharks away from public beaches.

neuromasts The hairs that send messages to the lateral line of a shark's nervous system when it senses vibrations.

overfishing The practice of fishing too much for a species, leading to its near endangerment.

pectoral fin Any one of two paired flippers at the front of a shark's body.

pelvic fin One of the fin pairs near the back of a shark.

predator An animal that hunts, kills, and eats other animals. Its victims are called prey.

ray The shark's closest relative. Its body is flat, and its fins are shaped like wings.

requiem A class of streamlined, fast-swimming sharks that most people consider typical sharks.

Index

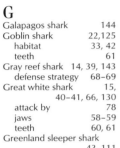
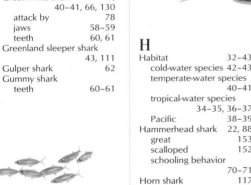

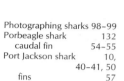

Acknowledgments

TEXT

The text for this publication has been drawn from research provided by George H. Burgess, Leonard J.V. Compagno, Carson Creagh, Kevin Deacon, Guido Dingerkus, Richard Ellis, Edward S. Hodgson, Kin Holland, Roland Hughes, C. Scott Johnson, Peter Last, John E. McKosker, Chadwick S. Macfie, John G. Maisey, Richard Martin, Arthur A. Myrberg Jr., A.M. Olsen, Larry J. Paul, Colin Simpfendorfer, Marty Snyderman, John D. Stevens, Leighton R. Taylor Jr., Valerie Taylor, Timothy C. Tricas, Terence I. Walker, and John West.

PHOTOGRAPH CREDITS

SH = Shutterstock; iS = istockphoto.com

17 SH **26** SH **29** SH **32** SH **34** SH **70** SH **78** SH **86** iS

ILLUSTRATION AND MAPS

Martin Camm, Greg Gampbell, Chris Forsey, Ray Grinaway, Gino Hasler, Frank Knight, Lorenzo Lucia, Tony Pyrzakowski, Roger Swainston, Steve Trevaskis, Genevieve Wallace, Rod Westblade

CONSULTANT

Leighton R. Taylor is a Fellow of the California Academy of Sciences and a Research Associate of the Bishop Museum of Waikiki Aquarium in Hawaii.

SPECIAL THANKS

Annye Bone, Caroline Comerford, Kat Engh, Hayden Foell, Jason Vance